Kendall Hunt | iM Illustrative Mathematics CERTIFIED

STUDENT EDITION
Book 3

Units

7 | 8 | 9

GRADE 6

iM Illustrative Mathematics®
LEARN MATH FOR LIFE

ISBN 978-1-7924-0184-8

MS3.1415

20211203

Let's Put it to Work

Let's Put it to Work

GRADE 6

Unit

7

STUDENT EDITION
Book 3

Kendall Hunt |

Lesson 1: Positive and Negative Numbers

Let's explore how we represent temperatures and elevations.

1.1: Notice and Wonder: Memphis and Bangor

Memphis, TN
Saturday 5:00 PM
Light Rain Showers

37°F

3°C

Bangor, ME
Saturday 6:00 PM
Partly Cloudy

1°F

-17°C

What do you notice? What do you wonder?

1.2: Above and Below Zero

1. Here are three situations involving changes in temperature and three number lines. Represent each change on a number line. Then, answer the question.

   a. At noon, the temperature was 5 degrees Celsius. By late afternoon, it has risen 6 degrees Celsius. What was the temperature late in the afternoon?

   b. The temperature was 8 degrees Celsius at midnight. By dawn, it has dropped 12 degrees Celsius. What was the temperature at dawn?

   c. Water freezes at 0 degrees Celsius, but the freezing temperature can be lowered by adding salt to the water. A student discovered that adding half a cup of salt to a gallon of water lowers its freezing temperature by 7 degrees Celsius. What is the freezing temperature of the gallon of salt water?

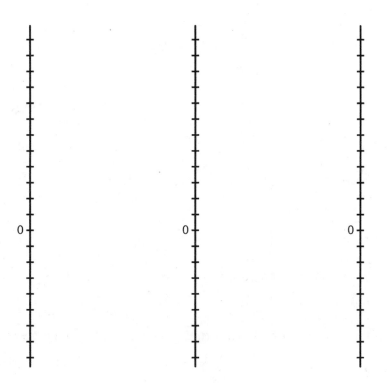

2. Discuss with a partner:

   a. How did each of you name the resulting temperature in each situation?

   b. What does it mean when the temperature is above 0? Below 0?

   c. Do numbers less than 0 make sense in other contexts? Give some specific examples to show how they do or do not make sense.

1.3: High Places, Low Places

1. Here is a table that shows elevations of various cities.

city	elevation (feet)
Harrisburg, PA	320
Bethell, IN	1,211
Denver, CO	5,280
Coachella, CA	-22
Death Valley, CA	-282
New York City, NY	33
Miami, FL	0

a. On the list of cities, which city has the second highest elevation?

b. How would you describe the elevation of Coachella, CA in relation to sea level?

c. How would you describe the elevation of Death Valley, CA in relation to sea level?

d. If you are standing on a beach right next to the ocean, what is your elevation?

e. How would you describe the elevation of Miami, FL?

f. A city has a higher elevation than Coachella, CA. Select all numbers that could represent the city's elevation. Be prepared to explain your reasoning.

- ■ -11 feet

- ■ -35 feet

- ■ 4 feet

- ■ -8 feet

- ■ 0 feet

2. Here are two tables that show the elevations of highest points on land and lowest points in the ocean. Distances are measured from sea level.

mountain	continent	elevation (meters)
Everest	Asia	8,848
Kilimanjaro	Africa	5,895
Denali	North America	6,168
Pikchu Pikchu	South America	5,664

trench	ocean	elevation (meters)
Mariana Trench	Pacific	-11,033
Puerto Rico Trench	Atlantic	-8,600
Tonga Trench	Pacific	-10,882
Sunda Trench	Indian	-7,725

a. Which point in the ocean is the lowest in the world? What is its elevation?

b. Which mountain is the highest in the world? What is its elevation?

c. If you plot the elevations of the mountains and trenches on a vertical number line, what would 0 represent? What would points above 0 represent? What about points below 0?

d. Which is farther from sea level: the deepest point in the ocean, or the top of the highest mountain in the world? Explain.

Are you ready for more?

A spider spins a web in the following way:

- It starts at sea level.
- It moves up one inch in the first minute.
- It moves down two inches in the second minute.
- It moves up three inches in the third minute.
- It moves down four inches in the fourth minute.

Assuming that the pattern continues, what will the spider's elevation be after an hour has passed?

Lesson 1 Summary

Positive numbers are numbers that are greater than 0. **Negative numbers** are numbers that are less than zero. The meaning of a negative number in a context depends on the meaning of zero in that context.

For example, if we measure temperatures in degrees Celsius, then 0 degrees Celsius corresponds to the temperature at which water freezes.

In this context, positive temperatures are warmer than the freezing point and negative temperatures are colder than the freezing point. A temperature of -6 degrees Celsius means that it is 6 degrees away from 0 and it is less than 0. This thermometer shows a temperature of -6 degrees Celsius.

If the temperature rises a few degrees and gets very close to 0 degrees without reaching it, the temperature is still a negative number.

iM KH

Another example is elevation, which is a distance above or below sea level. An elevation of 0 refers to the sea level. Positive elevations are higher than sea level, and negative elevations are lower than sea level.

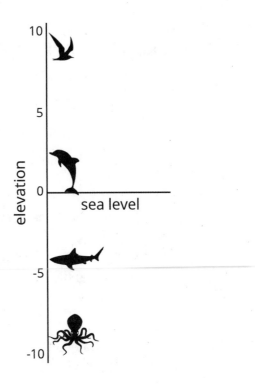

Glossary

- negative number
- positive number

Lesson 1 Practice Problems

1. a. Is a temperature of -11 degrees warmer or colder than a temperature of -15 degrees?

   b. Is an elevation of -10 feet closer or farther from the surface of the ocean than an elevation of -8 feet?

   c. It was 8 degrees at nightfall. The temperature dropped 10 degrees by midnight. What was the temperature at midnight?

   d. A diver is 25 feet below sea level. After he swims up 15 feet toward the surface, what is his elevation?

2. a. A whale is at the surface of the ocean to breathe. What is the whale's elevation?

   b. The whale swims down 300 feet to feed. What is the whale's elevation now?

   c. The whale swims down 150 more feet more. What is the whale's elevation now?

   d. Plot each of the three elevations as a point on a vertical number line. Label each point with its numeric value.

3. Explain how to calculate a number that is equal to $\frac{2.1}{1.5}$.

(From Unit 6, Lesson 5.)

iM KH

4. Write an equation to represent each situation and then solve the equation.

   a. Andre drinks 15 ounces of water, which is $\frac{3}{5}$ of a bottle. How much does the bottle hold? Use x for the number of ounces of water the bottle holds.

   b. A bottle holds 15 ounces of water. Jada drank 8.5 ounces of water. How many ounces of water are left in the bottle? Use y for the number of ounces of water left in the bottle.

   c. A bottle holds z ounces of water. A second bottle holds 16 ounces, which is $\frac{8}{5}$ times as much water. How much does the first bottle hold?

   (From Unit 6, Lesson 4.)

5. A rectangle has an area of 24 square units and a side length of $2\frac{3}{4}$ units. Find the other side length of the rectangle. Show your reasoning.

   (From Unit 4, Lesson 13.)

Lesson 2: Points on the Number Line

Let's plot positive and negative numbers on the number line.

2.1: A Point on the Number Line

Which of the following numbers could be *B*?

2.5 $\frac{2}{5}$ $\frac{5}{2}$ $\frac{25}{10}$ 2.49

2.2: What's the Temperature?

1. Here are five thermometers. The first four thermometers show temperatures in Celsius. Write the temperatures in the blanks.

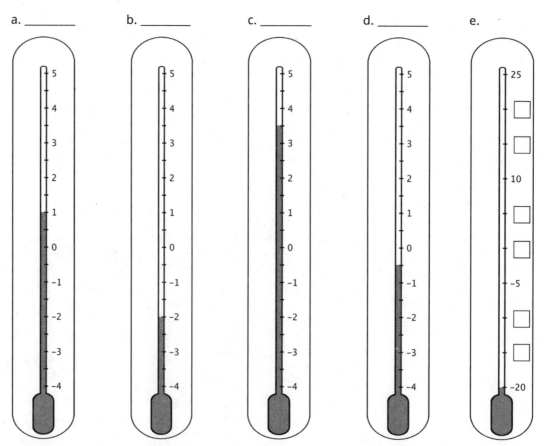

The last thermometer is missing some numbers. Write them in the boxes.

iM KH

2. Elena says that the thermometer shown here reads
   -2.5°C because the line of the liquid is above -2°C. Jada
   says that it is -1.5°C. Do you agree with either one of
   them? Explain your reasoning.

3. One morning, the temperature in Phoenix, Arizona, was 8°C and the temperature in
   Portland, Maine, was 12°C cooler. What was the temperature in Portland?

2.3: Folded Number Lines

Your teacher will give you a sheet of tracing paper on which to draw a number line.

1. Follow the steps to make your own number line.

   ○ Use a straightedge or a ruler to draw a horizontal line. Mark the middle point of
     the line and label it 0.

   ○ To the right of 0, draw tick marks that are 1 centimeter apart. Label the tick
     marks 1, 2, 3. . . 10. This represents the positive side of your number line.

   ○ Fold your paper so that a vertical crease goes through 0 and the two sides of the
     number line match up perfectly.

   ○ Use the fold to help you trace the tick marks that you already drew onto the
     opposite side of the number line. Unfold and label the tick marks -1, -2, -3. . .
     -10. This represents the negative side of your number line.

2. Use your number line to answer these questions:

    a. Which number is the same distance away from zero as is the number 4?

    b. Which number is the same distance away from zero as is the number -7?

    c. Two numbers that are the same distance from zero on the number line are called **opposites**. Find another pair of opposites on the number line.

    d. Determine how far away the number 5 is from 0. Then, choose a positive number and a negative number that is each farther away from zero than is the number 5.

    e. Determine how far away the number -2 is from 0. Then, choose a positive number and a negative number that is each farther away from zero than is the number -2.

Pause here so your teacher can review your work.

3. Here is a number line with some points labeled with letters. Determine the location of points P, X, and Y.

If you get stuck, trace the number line and points onto a sheet of tracing paper, fold it so that a vertical crease goes through 0, and use the folded number line to help you find the unknown values.

Are you ready for more?

At noon, the temperatures in Portland, Maine, and Phoenix, Arizona, had opposite values. The temperature in Portland was $18°C$ lower than in Phoenix. What was the temperature in each city? Explain your reasoning.

Lesson 2 Summary

Here is a number line labeled with positive and negative numbers. The number 4 is positive, so its location is 4 units to the right of 0 on the number line. The number -1.1 is negative, so its location is 1.1 units to the left of 0 on the number line.

We say that the *opposite* of 8.3 is -8.3, and that the *opposite* of $\frac{-3}{2}$ is $\frac{3}{2}$. Any pair of numbers that are equally far from 0 are called **opposites**.

Points A and B are opposites because they are both 2.5 units away from 0, even though A is to the left of 0 and B is to the right of 0.

A positive number has a negative number for its opposite. A negative number has a positive number for its opposite. The opposite of 0 is itself.

You have worked with positive numbers for many years. All of the positive numbers you have seen—whole and non-whole numbers—can be thought of as fractions and can be located on a the number line.

To locate a non-whole number on a number line, we can divide the distance between two whole numbers into fractional parts and then count the number of parts. For example, 2.7 can be written as $2\frac{7}{10}$. The segment between 2 and 3 can be partitioned into 10 equal parts or 10 tenths. From 2, we can count 7 of the tenths to locate 2.7 on the number line.

All of the fractions and their opposites are what we call **rational numbers**. For example, 4, -1.1, 8.3, -8.3, $\frac{-3}{2}$, and $\frac{3}{2}$ are all rational numbers.

Glossary

- opposite
- rational number

Lesson 2 Practice Problems

1. For each number, name its opposite.

   a. -5

   b. 28

   c. -10.4

   a. 0.875

   b. 0

   c. -8,003

2. Plot the numbers -1.5, $\frac{3}{2}$, -$\frac{3}{2}$, and -$\frac{4}{3}$ on the number line. Label each point with its numeric value.

3. Plot these points on a number line.

   ○ -1.5

   ○ the opposite of -2

   ○ the opposite of 0.5

   ○ -2

4.   a. Represent each of these temperatures in degrees Fahrenheit with a positive or negative number.

   ■ 5 degrees above zero

   ■ 3 degrees below zero

   ■ 6 degrees above zero

   ■ $2\frac{3}{4}$ degrees below zero

   b. Order the temperatures above from the coldest to the warmest.

   (From Unit 7, Lesson 1.)

iM KH

5. Solve each equation.

a. $8x = \frac{2}{3}$

b. $1\frac{1}{2} = 2x$

c. $5x = \frac{2}{7}$

d. $\frac{1}{4}x = 5$

e. $\frac{1}{5} = \frac{2}{3}x$

(From Unit 6, Lesson 5.)

6. Write the solution to each equation as a fraction and as a decimal.

a. $2x = 3$

b. $5y = 3$

c. $0.3z = 0.009$

(From Unit 6, Lesson 5.)

7. There are 15.24 centimeters in 6 inches.

a. How many centimeters are in 1 foot?

b. How many centimeters are in 1 yard?

(From Unit 3, Lesson 4.)

Lesson 3: Comparing Positive and Negative Numbers

Let's compare numbers on the number line.

3.1: Which One Doesn't Belong: Inequalities

Which inequality doesn't belong?

- $\frac{5}{4} < 2$

- $8.5 > 0.95$

- $8.5 < 7$

- $10.00 < 100$

3.2: Comparing Temperatures

Here are the low temperatures, in degrees Celsius, for a week in Anchorage, Alaska.

day	Mon	Tues	Weds	Thurs	Fri	Sat	Sun
temperature	5	-1	-5.5	-2	3	4	0

1. Plot the temperatures on a number line. Which day of the week had the lowest low temperature?

iM KH

2. The lowest temperature ever recorded in the United States was -62 degrees Celsius, in Prospect Creek Camp, Alaska. The average temperature on Mars is about -55 degrees Celsius.

   a. Which is warmer, the coldest temperature recorded in the USA, or the average temperature on Mars? Explain how you know.

   b. Write an inequality to show your answer.

3. On a winter day the low temperature in Anchorage, Alaska, was -21 degrees Celsius and the low temperature in Minneapolis, Minnesota, was -14 degrees Celsius.

   Jada said, "I know that 14 is less than 21, so -14 is also less than -21. This means that it was colder in Minneapolis than in Anchorage."

   Do you agree? Explain your reasoning.

Are you ready for more?

Another temperature scale frequently used in science is the *Kelvin scale*. In this scale, 0 is the lowest possible temperature of anything in the universe, and it is -273.15 degrees in the Celsius scale. Each 1 K is the same as 1°C, so 10 K is the same as -263.15°C.

   1. Water boils at 100°C. What is this temperature in K?

   2. Ammonia boils at -35.5°C. What is the boiling point of ammonia in K?

   3. Explain why only positive numbers (and 0) are needed to record temperature in K.

3.3: Rational Numbers on a Number Line

1. Plot the numbers -2, 4, -7, and 10 on the number line. Label each point with its numeric value.

2. Decide whether each inequality statement is true or false. Be prepared to explain your reasoning.

    a. -2 < 4

    b. -2 < -7

    c. 4 > -7

    d. -7 > 10

3. Andre says that $\frac{1}{4}$ is less than $-\frac{3}{4}$ because, of the two numbers, $\frac{1}{4}$ is closer to 0. Do you agree? Explain your reasoning.

4. Answer each question. Be prepared to explain how you know.

    a. Which number is greater: $\frac{1}{4}$ or $\frac{5}{4}$?

    b. Which is farther from 0: $\frac{1}{4}$ or $\frac{5}{4}$?

    c. Which number is greater: $-\frac{3}{4}$ or $\frac{5}{8}$?

    d. Which is farther from 0: $-\frac{3}{4}$ or $\frac{5}{8}$?

iM KH

e. Is the number that is farther from 0 always the greater number? Explain your reasoning.

Lesson 3 Summary

We use the words *greater than* and *less than* to compare numbers on the number line. For example, the numbers -2.7, 0.8, and -1.3, are shown on the number line.

Because -2.7 is to the left of -1.3, we say that -2.7 is less than -1.3. We write:

$$-2.7 < -1.3$$

In general, any number that is to the left of a number n is less than n.

We can see that -1.3 is greater than -2.7 because -1.3 is to the right of -2.7. We write:

$$-1.3 > -2.7$$

In general, any number that is to the right of a number n is greater than n

We can also see that $0.8 > -1.3$ and $0.8 > -2.7$. In general, any positive number is greater than any negative number.

Glossary

- sign

Lesson 3 Practice Problems

1. Decide whether each inequality statement is true or false. Explain your reasoning.

    a. -5 > 2

    b. 3 > -8

    c. -12 > -15

    d. -12.5 > -12

2. Here is a true statement: -8.7 < -8.4. Select **all** of the statements that are equivalent to -8.7 < -8.4.

    A. -8.7 is further to the right on the number line than -8.4.

    B. -8.7 is further to the left on the number line than -8.4.

    C. -8.7 is less than -8.4.

    D. -8.7 is greater than -8.4.

    E. -8.4 is less than -8.7.

    F. -8.4 is greater than -8.7.

3. Plot each of the following numbers on the number line. Label each point with its numeric value. 0.4, -1.5, $-1\frac{7}{10}$, $-\frac{11}{10}$

(From Unit 7, Lesson 2.)

iM KH

4. The table shows five states and the lowest point in each state.

Put the states in order by their lowest elevation, from least to greatest.

state	lowest elevation (feet)
California	-282
Colorado	3350
Louisiana	-8
New Mexico	2842
Wyoming	3099

(From Unit 7, Lesson 4.)

5. Each lap around the track is 400 meters.

    a. How many meters does someone run if they run:

       2 laps?   5 laps? x laps?

    b. If Noah ran 14 laps, how many meters did he run?

    c. If Noah ran 7,600 meters, how many laps did he run?

(From Unit 6, Lesson 6.)

6. A stadium can seat 16,000 people at full capacity.

    a. If there are 13,920 people in the stadium, what percentage of the capacity is filled? Explain or show your reasoning.

    b. What percentage of the capacity is not filled?

(From Unit 3, Lesson 16.)

Lesson 4: Ordering Rational Numbers

Let's order rational numbers.

4.1: How Do They Compare?

Use the symbols >, <, or = to compare each pair of numbers. Be prepared to explain your reasoning.

- 12 _____ 19

- 15 _____ 1.5

- 6.050 _____ 6.05

- $\frac{19}{24}$ _____ $\frac{19}{21}$

- 212 _____ 190

- 9.02 _____ 9.2

- 0.4 _____ $\frac{9}{40}$

- $\frac{16}{17}$ _____ $\frac{11}{12}$

4.2: Ordering Rational Number Cards

Your teacher will give you a set of number cards. Order them from least to greatest.

Your teacher will give you a second set of number cards. Add these to the correct places in the ordered set.

iM KH

4.3: Comparing Points on A Line

1.

Use each of the following terms at least once to describe or compare the values of points M, N, P, R.

- greater than
- less than
- opposite of (or opposites)
- negative number

2. Tell what the value of each point would be if:

a. P is $2\frac{1}{2}$

b. N is -0.4

c. R is 200

d. M is -15

Are you ready for more?

The list of fractions between 0 and 1 with denominators between 1 and 3 looks like this:

$$\frac{0}{1}, \frac{1}{1}, \frac{1}{2}, \frac{1}{3}, \frac{2}{3}$$

We can put them in order like this: $\frac{0}{1} < \frac{1}{3} < \frac{1}{2} < \frac{2}{3} < \frac{1}{1}$

Now let's expand the list to include fractions with denominators of 4. We won't include $\frac{2}{4}$, because $\frac{1}{2}$ is already on the list.

$$\frac{0}{1} < \frac{1}{4} < \frac{1}{3} < \frac{1}{2} < \frac{2}{3} < \frac{3}{4} < \frac{1}{1}$$

1. Expand the list again to include fractions that have denominators of 5.

2. Expand the list you made to include fractions have have denominators of 6.

3. When you add a new fraction to the list, you put it in between two "neighbors." Go back and look at your work. Do you see a relationship between a new fraction and its two neighbors?

Lesson 4 Summary

To order rational numbers from least to greatest, we list them in the order they appear on the number line from left to right. For example, we can see that the numbers

$$-2.7, -1.3, 0.8$$

are listed from least to greatest because of the order they appear on the number line.

iM **KH**

Lesson 4 Practice Problems

1. Select **all** of the numbers that are *greater than* -5.

   A. 1.3

   B. -6

   C. -12

   D. $\frac{1}{7}$

   E. -1

   F. -4

2. Order these numbers from least to greatest: $\frac{1}{2}$, 0, 1, $-1\frac{1}{2}$, $-\frac{1}{2}$, -1

3. Here are the boiling points of certain elements in degrees Celsius:

   ○ Argon: -185.8
   ○ Chlorine: -34
   ○ Fluorine: -188.1
   ○ Hydrogen: -252.87
   ○ Krypton: -153.2

   List the elements from least to greatest boiling points.

4. Explain why zero is considered its own opposite.

   (From Unit 7, Lesson 2.)

5. Explain how to make these calculations mentally.

   a. $99 + 54$

   b. $244 - 99$

   c. $99 \cdot 6$

   d. $99 \cdot 15$

   (From Unit 6, Lesson 9.)

6. Find the quotients.

   a. $\frac{1}{2} \div 2$

   b. $2 \div 2$

   c. $\frac{1}{2} \div \frac{1}{2}$

   d. $\frac{38}{79} \div \frac{38}{79}$

   (From Unit 4, Lesson 11.)

7. Over several months, the weight of a baby measured in pounds doubles. Does its weight measured in kilograms also double? Explain.

   (From Unit 3, Lesson 4.)

iM KH

Lesson 5: Using Negative Numbers to Make Sense of Contexts

Let's make sense of negative amounts of money.

5.1: Notice and Wonder: It Comes and Goes

activity	amount
do my chores	30.00
babysit my cousin	45.00
buy my lunch	-10.80
get my allowance	15.00
buy a shirt	-18.69
pet my dog	0.00

What do you notice? What do you wonder?

5.2: The Concession Stand

The manager of the concession stand keeps records of all of the supplies she buys and all of the items she sells. The table shows some of her records for Tuesday.

item	quantity	value in dollars
doughnuts	-58	37.70
straws	3,000	-10.35
hot dogs	-39	48.75
pizza	13	-116.87
apples	-40	14.00
french fries	-88	132.00

1. Which items did she sell? Explain your reasoning.

2. How can we interpret -58 in this situation?

3. How can we interpret -10.35 in this situation?

4. On which item did she spend the most amount of money? Explain your reasoning.

iM KH

5.3: Drinks for Sale

A vending machine in an office building sells bottled beverages. The machine keeps track of all changes in the number of bottles from sales and from machine refills and maintenance. This record shows the changes for every 5-minute period over one hour.

1. What might a positive number mean in this context? What about a negative number?

2. What would a "0" in the second column mean in this context?

3. Which numbers—positive or negative—result in fewer bottles in the machine?

4. At what time was there the greatest change to the number of bottles in the machine? How did that change affect the number of remaining bottles in the machine?

5. At which time period, 8:05–8:09 or 8:25–8:29, was there a greater change to the number of bottles in the machine? Explain your reasoning.

time	number of bottles
8:00–8:04	-1
8:05–8:09	+12
8:10–8:14	-4
8:15–8:19	-1
8:20–8:24	-5
8:25–8:29	-12
8:30–8:34	-2
8:35–8:39	0
8:40–8:44	0
8:45–8:49	-6
8:50–8:54	+24
8:55–8:59	0
service	

6. The machine must be emptied to be serviced. If there are 40 bottles in the machine when it is to be serviced, what number will go in the second column in the table?

Are you ready for more?

Priya, Mai, and Lin went to a cafe on a weekend. Their shared bill came to $25. Each student gave the server a $10 bill. The server took this $30 and brought back five $1 bills in change. Each student took $1 back, leaving the rest, $2, as a tip for the server.

As she walked away from the cafe, Lin thought, "Wait—this doesn't make sense. Since I put in $10 and got $1 back, I wound up paying $9. So did Mai and Priya. Together, we paid $27. Then we left a $2 tip. That makes $29 total. And yet we originally gave the waiter $30. Where did the extra dollar go?"

Think about the situation and about Lin's question. Do you agree that the numbers didn't add up properly? Explain your reasoning.

Lesson 5 Summary

Sometimes we represent changes in a quantity with positive and negative numbers. If the quantity increases, the change is positive. If it decreases, the change is negative.

- Suppose 5 gallons of water is put in a washing machine. We can represent the change in the number of gallons as +5. If 3 gallons is emptied from the machine, we can represent the change as -3.

It is especially common to represent money we receive with positive numbers and money we spend with negative numbers.

- Suppose Clare gets $30.00 for her birthday and spends $18.00 buying lunch for herself and a friend. To her, the value of the gift can be represented as +30.00 and the value of the lunch as -18.00.

Whether a number is considered positive or negative depends on a person's perspective. If Clare's grandmother gives her $20 for her birthday, Clare might see this as +20, because to her, the amount of money she has increased. But her grandmother might see it as -20, because to her, the amount of money she has decreased.

In general, when using positive and negative numbers to represent changes, we have to be very clear about what it means when the change is positive and what it means when the change is negative.

Lesson 5 Practice Problems

1. Write a positive or negative number to represent each change in the high temperature.

   a. Tuesday's high temperature was 4 degrees less than Monday's high temperature.

   b. Wednesday's high temperature was 3.5 degrees less than Tuesday's high temperature.

   c. Thursday's high temperature was 6.5 degrees more than Wednesday's high temperature.

   d. Friday's high temperature was 2 degrees less than Thursday's high temperature.

2. Decide which of the following quantities can be represented by a positive number and which can be represented by a negative number. Give an example of a quantity with the opposite sign in the same situation.

   a. Tyler's puppy gained 5 pounds.

   b. The aquarium leaked 2 gallons of water.

   c. Andre received a gift of $10.

   d. Kiran gave a gift of $10.

   e. A climber descended 550 feet.

3. Make up a situation where a quantity is changing.

   a. Explain what it means to have a negative change.

   b. Explain what it means to have a positive change.

   c. Give an example of each.

4.   a. On the number line, label the points that are 4 units away from 0.

   b. If you fold the number line so that a vertical crease goes through 0, the points you label would match up. Explain why this happens.

   c. On the number line, label the points that are $\frac{5}{2}$ units from 0. What is the distance between these points?

   (From Unit 7, Lesson 2.)

5. Evaluate each expression.

   ○ $2^3 \cdot 3$ ○ $6^2 \div 4$

   ○ $\frac{4^2}{2}$ ○ $2^3 - 2$

   ○ 3^1 ○ $10^2 + 5^2$

   (From Unit 6, Lesson 12.)

iM KH

Lesson 6: Absolute Value of Numbers

Let's explore distances from zero more closely.

6.1: Number Talk: Closer to Zero

For each pair of expressions, decide mentally which one has a value that is closer to 0.

$\frac{9}{11}$ or $\frac{15}{11}$

$\frac{1}{5}$ or $\frac{1}{9}$

1.25 or $\frac{5}{4}$

0.01 or 0.001

6.2: Jumping Flea

1. A flea is jumping around on a number line.

    a. If the flea starts at 1 and jumps 4 units to the right, where does it end up? How far away from 0 is this?

    b. If the flea starts at 1 and jumps 4 units to the left, where does it end up? How far away from 0 is this?

    c. If the flea starts at 0 and jumps 3 units away, where might it land?

    d. If the flea jumps 7 units and lands at 0, where could it have started?

    e. The **absolute value** of a number is the distance it is from 0. The flea is currently to the left of 0 and the absolute value of its location is 4. Where on the number line is it?

    f. If the flea is to the left of 0 and the absolute value of its location is 5, where on the number line is it?

    g. If the flea is to the right of 0 and the absolute value of its location is 2.5, where on the number line is it?

2. We use the notation $|-2|$ to say "the absolute value of -2," which means "the distance of -2 from 0 on the number line."

    a. What does $|-7|$ mean and what is its value?

    b. What does $|1.8|$ mean and what is its value?

iM KH

6.3: Absolute Elevation and Temperature

1. A part of the city of New Orleans is 6 feet below sea level. We can use "-6 feet" to describe its elevation, and "|-6| feet" to describe its vertical distance from sea level. In the context of elevation, what would each of the following numbers describe?

    a. 25 feet

    b. |25| feet

    c. -8 feet

    d. |-8| feet

2. The elevation of a city is different from sea level by 10 feet. Name the two elevations that the city could have.

3. We write "-5°C" to describe a temperature that is 5 degrees Celsius below freezing point and "5°C" for a temperature that is 5 degrees above freezing. In this context, what do each of the following numbers describe?

    a. 1°C

    b. -4°C

    c. |12|°C

    d. |-7|°C

4.   a. Which temperature is colder: -6°C or 3°C?

    b. Which temperature is closer to freezing temperature: -6°C or 3°C?

    c. Which temperature has a smaller absolute value? Explain how you know.

Are you ready for more?

At a certain time, the difference between the temperature in New York City and in Boston was 7 degrees Celsius. The difference between the temperature in Boston and in Chicago was also 7 degrees Celsius. Was the temperature in New York City the same as the temperature in Chicago? Explain your answer.

Lesson 6 Summary

We compare numbers by comparing their positions on the number line: the one farther to the right is greater; the one farther to the left is less.

Sometimes we wish to compare which one is closer to or farther from 0. For example, we may want to know how far away the temperature is from the freezing point of $0°C$, regardless of whether it is above or below freezing.

The **absolute value** of a number tells us its distance from 0.

The absolute value of -4 is 4, because -4 is 4 units to the left of 0. The absolute value of 4 is also 4, because 4 is 4 units to the right of 0. Opposites always have the same absolute value because they both have the same distance from 0.

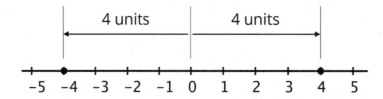

The distance from 0 to itself is 0, so the absolute value of 0 is 0. Zero is the *only* number whose distance to 0 is 0. For all other absolute values, there are always two numbers—one positive and one negative—that have that distance from 0.

To say "the absolute value of 4," we write:
$$|4|$$

To say that "the absolute value of -8 is 8," we write:
$$|\text{-}8| = 8$$

Glossary
- absolute value

iM KH

Lesson 6 Practice Problems

1. On the number line, plot and label all numbers with an absolute value of $\frac{3}{2}$.

2. The temperature at dawn is $6°C$ away from 0. Select **all** the temperatures that are possible.

    A. -12°C

    B. -6°C

    C. 0°C

    D. 6°C

    E. 12°C

3. Put these numbers in order, from least to greatest.

    |-2.7| 0   1.3 |-1| 2

4. Lin's family needs to travel 325 miles to reach her grandmother's house.

    a. At 26 miles, what percentage of the trip's distance have they completed?

    b. How far have they traveled when they have completed 72% of the trip's distance?

    c. At 377 miles, what percentage of the trip's distance have they completed?

    (From Unit 5, Lesson 11.)

5. Elena donates some money to charity whenever she earns money as a babysitter. The table shows how much money, d, she donates for different amounts of money, m, that she earns.

d	4.44	1.80	3.12	3.60	2.16
m	37	15	26	30	18

a. What percent of her income does Elena donate to charity? Explain or show your work.

b. Which quantity, m or d, would be the better choice for the dependent variable in an equation describing the relationship between m and d? Explain your reasoning.

c. Use your choice from the second question to write an equation that relates m and d.

(From Unit 6, Lesson 16.)

6. How many times larger is the first number in the pair than the second?

a. 3^4 is _____ times larger than 3^3.

b. 5^3 is _____ times larger than 5^2.

c. 7^{10} is _____ times larger than 7^8.

d. 17^6 is _____ times larger than 17^4.

e. 5^{10} is _____ times larger than 5^4.

(From Unit 6, Lesson 12.)

iM KH

Lesson 7: Comparing Numbers and Distance from Zero

Let's use absolute value and negative numbers to think about elevation.

7.1: Opposites

1. a is a rational number. Choose a value for a and plot it on the number line.

2.   a. Based on where you plotted a, plot $-a$ on the same number line.

   b. What is the value of $-a$ that you plotted?

3. Noah said, "If a is a rational number, $-a$ will always be a negative number." Do you agree with Noah? Explain your reasoning.

7.2: Submarine

A submarine is at an elevation of -100 feet (100 feet below sea level). Let's compare the elevations of these four people to that of the submarine:

- Clare's elevation is greater than the elevation of the submarine. Clare is farther from sea level than the submarine.
- Andre's elevation is less than the elevation of the submarine. Andre is farther away from sea level than the submarine.
- Han's elevation is greater than the elevation of the submarine. Han is closer to sea level than is the submarine.
- Lin's elevation is the same distance away from sea level as the submarine's.

1. Complete the table as follows.

   a. Write a possible elevation for each person.

   b. Use $<$, $>$, or $=$ to compare the elevation of that person to that of the submarine.

   c. Use absolute value to tell how far away the person is from sea level (elevation 0).

   As an example, the first row has been filled with a possible elevation for Clare.

	possible elevation	compare to submarine	distance from sea level
Clare	150 feet	150 > -100	|150| or 150 feet
Andre			
Han			
Lin			

2. Priya says her elevation is less than the submarine's and she is closer to sea level. Is this possible? Explain your reasoning.

iM KH

7.3: Info Gap: Points on the Number Line

Your teacher will give you either a *problem card* or a *data card*. Do not show or read your card to your partner.

If your teacher gives you the *problem card*:

1. Silently read your card and think about what information you need to be able to answer the question.

2. Ask your partner for the specific information that you need.

3. Explain how you are using the information to solve the problem.

   Continue to ask questions until you have enough information to solve the problem.

4. Share the *problem card* and solve the problem independently.

5. Read the *data card* and discuss your reasoning.

If your teacher gives you the *data card*:

1. Silently read your card.

2. Ask your partner *"What specific information do you need?"* and wait for them to *ask* for information.

   If your partner asks for information that is not on the card, do not do the calculations for them. Tell them you don't have that information.

3. Before sharing the information, ask *"Why do you need that information?"* Listen to your partner's reasoning and ask clarifying questions.

4. Read the *problem card* and solve the problem independently.

5. Share the *data card* and discuss your reasoning.

7.4: Inequality Mix and Match

Here are some numbers and inequality symbols. Work with your partner to write true comparison statements.

-0.7	$-\frac{3}{5}$	1	4	$|-8|$	<
$-\frac{6}{3}$	-2.5	2.5	8	$|0.7|$	=
-4	0	$\frac{7}{2}$	$|3|$	$\left|-\frac{5}{2}\right|$	>

One partner should select two numbers and one comparison symbol and use them to write a true statement using symbols. The other partner should write a sentence in words with the same meaning, using the following phrases:

- is equal to
- is the absolute value of
- is greater than
- is less than

For example, one partner could write 4 < 8 and the other would write, "4 is less than 8." Switch roles until each partner has three true mathematical statements and three sentences written down.

iM KH

Are you ready for more?

For each question, choose a value for each variable to make the whole statement true. (When the word *and* is used in math, both parts have to be true for the whole statement to be true.) Can you do it if one variable is negative and one is positive? Can you do it if both values are negative?

1. $x < y$ and $|x| < y$.

2. $a < b$ and $|a| < |b|$.

3. $c < d$ and $|c| > d$.

4. $t < u$ and $|t| > |u|$.

Lesson 7 Summary

We can use elevation to help us compare two rational numbers or two absolute values.

- Suppose an anchor has an elevation of -10 meters and a house has an elevation of 12 meters. To describe the anchor having a lower elevation than the house, we can write -10 < 12 and say "-10 is less than 12."

- The anchor is closer to sea level than the house is to sea level (or elevation of 0). To describe this, we can write $|-10| < |12|$ and say "the distance between -10 and 0 is less than the distance between 12 and 0."

We can use similar descriptions to compare rational numbers and their absolute values outside of the context of elevation.

- To compare the distance of -47.5 and 5.2 from 0, we can say: $|-47.5|$ is 47.5 units away from 0, and $|5.2|$ is 5.2 units away from 0, so $|-47.5| > |5.2|$.

- $|-18| > 4$ means that the absolute value of -18 is greater than 4. This is true because 18 is greater than 4.

Lesson 7 Practice Problems

1. In the context of elevation, what would |-7| feet mean?

2. Match the the statements written in English with the mathematical statements.

A. The number -4 is a distance of 4 units away from 0 on the number line.

B. The number -63 is more than 4 units away from 0 on the number line.

C. The number 4 is greater than the number -4.

D. The numbers 4 and -4 are the same distance away from 0 on the number line.

E. The number -63 is less than the number 4.

F. The number -63 is further away from 0 than the number 4 on the number line.

1. $|-63| > 4$

2. $-63 < 4$

3. $|-63| > |4|$

4. $|-4| = 4$

5. $4 > -4$

6. $|4| = |-4|$

3. Compare each pair of expressions using >, <, or =.

○ -32 _____ 15

○ $|-32|$ _____ $|15|$

○ 5 _____ -5

○ $|5|$ _____ $|-5|$

○ 2 _____ -17

○ 2 _____ $|-17|$

○ $|-27|$ _____ $|-45|$

○ $|-27|$ _____ -45

iM KH

4. Mai received and spent money in the following ways last month. For each example, write a signed number to represent the change in money from her perspective.

  a. Her grandmother gave her $25 in a birthday card.

  b. She earned $14 dollars babysitting.

  c. She spent $10 on a ticket to the concert.

  d. She donated $3 to a local charity

  e. She got $2 interest on money that was in her savings account.

(From Unit 7, Lesson 5.)

5. Here are the lowest temperatures recorded in the last 2 centuries for some US cities.

  ○ Death Valley, CA was -45°F in January of 1937.
  ○ Danbury, CT was -37°F in February of 1943.
  ○ Monticello, FL was -2°F in February of 1899.
  ○ East Saint Louis, IL was -36°F in January of 1999.
  ○ Greenville, GA was -17°F in January of 1940.

  a. Which of these states has the lowest record temperature?

  b. Which state has a lower record temperature, FL or GA?

  c. Which state has a lower record temperature, CT or IL?

  d. How many more degrees colder is the record temperature for GA than for FL?

(From Unit 7, Lesson 1.)

6. Find the quotients.

  a. $0.024 \div 0.015$

  b. $0.24 \div 0.015$

  c. $0.024 \div 0.15$

  d. $24 \div 15$

(From Unit 5, Lesson 13.)

Lesson 8: Writing and Graphing Inequalities

Let's write inequalities.

8.1: Estimate Heights of People

1. Here is a picture of a man.

    a. Name a number, in feet, that is clearly too high for this man's height.

    b. Name a number, in feet, that is clearly too low for his height.

    c. Make an estimate of his height.

Pause here for a class discussion.

2. Here is a picture of the same man standing next to a child.

If the man's actual height is 5 feet 10 inches, what can you say about the height of the child in this picture?

Be prepared to explain your reasoning.

iM KH

8.2: Stories about 9

1. Your teacher will give you a set of paper slips with four stories and questions involving the number 9. Match each question to three representations of the solution: a description or a list, a number line, or an inequality statement.

2. Compare your matching decisions with another group's. If there are disagreements, discuss until both groups come to an agreement. Then, record your final matching decisions here.

   a. A fishing boat can hold fewer than 9 people. How many people (x) can it hold?

   ■ Description or list:

   ■ Number line:

   ■ Inequality:

   b. Lin needs more than 9 ounces of butter to make cookies for her party. How many ounces of butter (x) would be enough?

   ■ Description or list:

   ■ Number line:

   ■ Inequality:

   c. A magician will perform her magic tricks only if there are at least 9 people in the audience. For how many people (x) will she perform her magic tricks?

   ■ Description or list:

   ■ Number line:

   ■ Inequality:

d. A food scale can measure up to 9 kilograms of weight. What weights (*x*) can the scale measure?

■ Description or list:

■ Number line:

■ Inequality:

8.3: How High and How Low Can It Be?

Here is a picture of a person and a basketball hoop. Based on the picture, what do you think are reasonable estimates for the maximum and minimum heights of the basketball hoop?

1. Complete the first blank in each sentence with an estimate, and the second blank with "taller" or "shorter."

   a. I estimate the *minimum* height of the basketball hoop to be _____ feet; this means the hoop cannot be _____ than this height.

   b. I estimate the *maximum* height of the basketball hoop to be _____ feet; this means the hoop cannot be _____ than this height.

2. Write two inequalities—one to show your estimate for the *minimum* height of the basketball hoop, and another for the *maximum* height. Use an inequality symbol and the variable *h* to represent the unknown height.

iM KH

3. Plot each estimate for minimum or maximum value on a number line.

   ○ Minimum:

   ○ Maximum:

4. Suppose a classmate estimated the value of h to be 19 feet. Does this estimate agree with your inequality for the maximum height? Does it agree with your inequality for the minimum height? Explain or show how you know.

5. Ask a partner for an estimate of h. Record the estimate and check if it agrees with your inequalities for maximum and minimum heights.

Are you ready for more?

1. Find 3 different numbers that a could be if $|a| < 5$. Plot these points on the number line. Then plot as many other possibilities for a as you can.

   -10 -9 -8 -7 -6 -5 -4 -3 -2 -1 0 1 2 3 4 5 6 7 8 9 10

2. Find 3 different numbers that b could be if $|b| > 3$. Plot these points on the number line. Then plot as many other possibilities for b as you can.

   -10 -9 -8 -7 -6 -5 -4 -3 -2 -1 0 1 2 3 4 5 6 7 8 9 10

Lesson 8 Summary

An inequality tells us that one value is *less than* or *greater than* another value.

Suppose we knew the temperature is *less than* 3°F, but we don't know exactly what it is. To represent what we know about the temperature t in °F we can write the inequality:

$$t < 3$$

The temperature can also be graphed on a number line. Any point to the left of 3 is a possible value for t. The open circle at 3 means that t cannot be *equal* to 3, because the temperature is *less than* 3.

Here is another example. Suppose a young traveler has to be at least 16 years old to fly on an airplane without an accompanying adult.

If a represents the age of the traveler, any number greater than 16 is a possible value for a, and 16 itself is also a possible value of a. We can show this on a number line by drawing a closed circle at 16 to show that it meets the requirement (a 16-year-old person can travel alone). From there, we draw a line that points to the right.

We can also write an inequality and equation to show possible values for a:

$$a > 16$$
$$a = 16$$

iM KH

Lesson 8 Practice Problems

1. At the book sale, all books cost less than $5.

    a. What is the most expensive a book could be?

    b. Write an inequality to represent costs of books at the sale.

    c. Draw a number line to represent the inequality.

2. Kiran started his homework *before* 7:00 p.m. and finished his homework *after* 8:00 p.m. Let h represent the number of hours Kiran worked on his homework.

    Decide if each statement it is definitely true, definitely not true, or possibly true. Explain your reasoning.

    a. $h > 1$

    b. $h > 2$

    c. $h < 1$

    d. $h < 2$

3. Consider a rectangular prism with length 4 and width and height d.

   a. Find an expression for the volume of the prism in terms of d.

   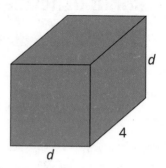

   b. Compute the volume of the prism when $d = 1$, when $d = 2$, and when $d = \frac{1}{2}$.

(From Unit 6, Lesson 14.)

4. Match the statements written in English with the mathematical statements. All of these statements are true.

   A. The number -15 is further away from 0 than the number -12 on the number line.

   B. The number -12 is a distance of 12 units away from 0 on the number line.

   C. The distance between -12 and 0 on the number line is greater than -15.

   D. The numbers 12 and -12 are the same distance away from 0 on the number line.

   E. The number -15 is less than the number -12.

   F. The number 12 is greater than the number -12.

   1. $|-12| > -15$

   2. $-15 < -12$

   3. $|-15| > |-12|$

   4. $|-12| = 12$

   5. $12 > -12$

   6. $|12| = |-12|$

(From Unit 7, Lesson 7.)

iM KH

5. Here are five sums. Use the distributive property to write each sum as a product with two factors.

  a. $2a + 7a$

  b. $5z - 10$

  c. $c - 2cd$

  d. $r + r + r + r$

  e. $2x - \frac{1}{2}$

  (From Unit 6, Lesson 11.)

Lesson 9: Solutions of Inequalities

Let's think about the solutions to inequalities.

9.1: Unknowns on a Number Line

The number line shows several points, each labeled with a letter.

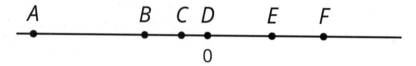

1. Fill in each blank with a letter so that the inequality statements are true.

   a. _____ > _____

   b. _____ < _____

2. Jada says that she found three different ways to complete the first question correctly. Do you think this is possible? Explain your reasoning.

3. List a possible value for each letter on the number line based on its location.

9.2: Amusement Park Rides

Priya finds these height requirements for some of the rides at an amusement park.

To ride the . . .	you must be . . .
High Bounce	between 55 and 72 inches tall
Climb-A-Thon	under 60 inches tall
Twirl-O-Coaster	58 inches minimum

1. Write an inequality for each of the the three height requirements. Use h for the unknown height. Then, represent each height requirement on a number line.

- High Bounce

- Climb-A-Thon

- Twirl-O-Coaster

Pause here for additional instructions from your teacher.

2. Han's cousin is 55 inches tall. Han doesn't think she is tall enough to ride the High Bounce, but Kiran believes that she is tall enough. Do you agree with Han or Kiran? Be prepared to explain your reasoning.

3. Priya can ride the Climb-A-Thon, but she cannot ride the High Bounce or the Twirl-O-Coaster. Which, if any, of the following could be Priya's height? Be prepared to explain your reasoning.

- 59 inches
- 53 inches
- 56 inches

4. Jada is 56 inches tall. Which rides can she go on?

5. Kiran is 60 inches tall. Which rides can he go on?

6. The inequalities $h < 75$ and $h > 64$ represent the height restrictions, in inches, of another ride. Write three values that are **solutions** to both of these inequalities.

Are you ready for more?

1. Represent the height restrictions for all three rides on a single number line, using a different color for each ride.

2. Which part of the number line is shaded with all 3 colors?

3. Name one possible height a person could be in order to go on all three rides.

9.3: What Number Am I?

Your teacher will give your group two sets of cards—one set shows inequalities and the other shows numbers. Place the inequality cards face up where everyone can see them. Shuffle the number cards and stack them face down.

To play:

- One person in your group is the detective. The other people will give clues.
- Pick one number card from the stack and show it to everyone except the detective.
- The people giving clues each choose an inequality that will help the detective identify the unknown number.
- The detective studies the inequalities and makes three guesses.

  - If the detective does not guess the right number, each person chooses another inequality to help.
  - When the detective does guess the right number, a new person becomes the detective.

- Repeat the game until everyone has had a turn being the detective.

Lesson 9 Summary

Let's say a movie ticket costs less than $10. If c represents the cost of a movie ticket, we can use $c < 10$ to express what we know about the cost of a ticket.

Any value of c that makes the inequality true is called a **solution to the inequality**.

For example, 5 is a solution to the inequality $c < 10$ because $5 < 10$ (or "5 is less than 10") is a true statement, but 12 is not a solution because $12 < 10$ ("12 is less than 10") is *not* a true statement.

If a situation involves more than one boundary or limit, we will need more than one inequality to express it.

For example, if we knew that it rained for *more* than 10 minutes but *less* than 30 minutes, we can describe the number of minutes that it rained (r) with the following inequalities and number lines.

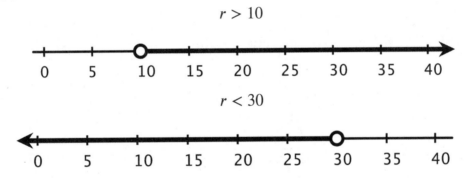

Any number of minutes greater than 10 is a solution to $r > 10$, and any number less than 30 is a solution to $r < 30$. But to meet the condition of "more than 10 but less than 30," the solutions are limited to the numbers between 10 and 30 minutes, *not* including 10 and 30.

We can show the solutions visually by graphing the two inequalities on one number line.

Glossary

- solution to an inequality

Lesson 9 Practice Problems

1. a. Select **all** numbers that are solutions to the inequality $k > 5$.

   | 4 | 5 | 6 | 5.2 | 5.01 | 0.5 |

   b. Draw a number line to represent this inequality.

2. A sign on the road says: "Speed limit, 60 miles per hour."

   a. Let s be the speed of a car. Write an inequality that matches the information on the sign.

   b. Draw a number line to represent the solutions to the inequality.

   c. Could 60 be a value of s? Explain your reasoning.

3. One day in Boston, MA, the high temperature was 60 degrees Fahrenheit, and the low temperature was 52 degrees.

   a. Write one or more inequalities to describe the temperatures T that are between the high and low temperature on that day.

   b. Show the possible temperatures on a number line.

iM **KH**

4. Select **all** the true statements.

   A. $-5 < |-5|$

   B. $|-6| < -5$

   C. $|-6| < 3$

   D. $4 < |-7|$

   E. $|-7| < |-8|$

   (From Unit 7, Lesson 7.)

5. Match each equation to its solution.

   a. $x^4 = 81$ ○ 2

   b. $x^2 = 100$ ○ 3

   c. $x^3 = 64$ ○ 4

   d. $x^5 = 32$ ○ 10

   (From Unit 6, Lesson 15.)

6.   a. The price of a cell phone is usually $250. Elena's mom buys one of these cell phones for $150. What percentage of the usual price did she pay?

      b. Elena's dad buys another type of cell phone that also usually sells for $250. He pays 75% of the usual price. How much did he pay?

      (From Unit 3, Lesson 14.)

Lesson 10: Interpreting Inequalities

Let's examine what inequalities can tell us.

10.1: True or False: Fractions and Decimals

Is each equation true or false? Be prepared to explain your reasoning.

1. $3(12 + 5) = (3 \cdot 12) \cdot (3 \cdot 5)$

2. $\frac{1}{3} \cdot \frac{3}{4} = \frac{3}{4} \cdot \frac{2}{6}$

3. $2 \cdot (1.5) \cdot 12 = 4 \cdot (0.75) \cdot 6$

10.2: Basketball Game

Noah scored n points in a basketball game.

1. What does $15 < n$ mean in the context of the basketball game?

2. What does $n < 25$ mean in the context of the basketball game?

3. Draw two number lines to represent the solutions to the two inequalities.

4. Name a possible value for n that is a solution to both inequalities.

5. Name a possible value for n that is a solution to $15 < n$, but not a solution to $n < 25$.

6. Can -8 be a solution to n in this context? Explain your reasoning.

iM KH

10.3: Unbalanced Hangers

1. Here is a diagram of an unbalanced hanger.

a. Jada says that the weight of one circle is greater than the weight of one pentagon. Write an inequality to represent her statement. Let p be the weight of one pentagon and c be the weight of one circle.

b. A circle weighs 12 ounces. Use this information to write another inequality to represent the relationship of the weights. Then, describe what this inequality means in this context.

2. Here is another diagram of an unbalanced hanger.

a. Write an inequality to represent the relationship of the weights. Let p be the weight of one pentagon and s be the weight of one square.

b. One pentagon weighs 8 ounces. Use this information to write another inequality to represent the relationship of the weights. Then, describe what this inequality means in this context.

c. Graph the solutions to this inequality on a number line.

3. Based on your work so far, can you tell the relationship between the weight of a square and the weight of a circle? If so, write an inequality to represent that relationship. If not, explain your reasoning.

4. This is another diagram of an unbalanced hanger.

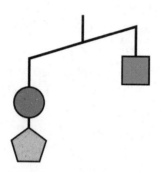

Andre writes the following inequality: $c + p < s$. Do you agree with his inequality? Explain your reasoning.

5. Jada looks at another diagram of an unbalanced hangar and writes: $s + c > 2t$, where t represents the weight of one triangle. Draw a sketch of the diagram.

Are you ready for more?

Here is a picture of a balanced hanger. It shows that the total weight of the three triangles is the same as the total weight of the four squares.

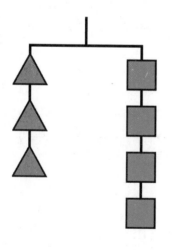

1. What does this tell you about the weight of one square when compared to one triangle? Explain how you know.

2. Write an equation or an inequality to describe the relationship between the weight of a square and that of a triangle. Let s be the weight of a square and t be the weight of a triangle.

Lesson 10 Summary

When we find the solutions to an inequality, we should think about its context carefully. A number may be a solution to an inequality outside of a context, but may not make sense when considered in context.

- Suppose a basketball player scored more than 11 points in a game, and we represent the number of points she scored, s, with the inequality $s > 11$. By looking only at $s > 11$, we can say that numbers such as 12, $14\frac{1}{2}$, and 130.25 are all solutions to the inequality because they each make the inequality true.

$$12 > 11 \qquad\qquad 14\frac{1}{2} > 11 \qquad\qquad 130.25 > 11$$

In a basketball game, however, it is only possible to score a whole number of points, so fractional and decimal scores are not possible. It is also highly unlikely that one person would score more than 130 points in a single game.

In other words, the context of an inequality may limit its solutions.

Here is another example:

- The solutions to $r < 30$ can include numbers such as $27\frac{3}{4}$, 18.5, 0, and -7. But if r represents the number of minutes of rain yesterday (and it did rain), then our solutions are limited to positive numbers. Zero or negative number of minutes would not make sense in this context.

To show the upper and lower boundaries, we can write two inequalities:

$$0 < r \qquad\qquad\qquad\qquad r < 30$$

Inequalities can also represent comparison of two unknown numbers.

- Let's say we knew that a puppy weighs more than a kitten, but we did not know the weight of either animal. We can represent the weight of the puppy, in pounds, with p and the weight of the kitten, in pounds, with k, and write this inequality:

$$p > k$$

Lesson 10 Practice Problems

1. There is a closed carton of eggs in Mai's refrigerator. The carton contains e eggs and it can hold 12 eggs.

    a. What does the inequality $e < 12$ mean in this context?

    b. What does the inequality $e > 0$ mean in this context?

    c. What are some possible values of e that will make both $e < 12$ and $e > 0$ true?

2. Here is a diagram of an unbalanced hanger.

    a. Write an inequality to represent the relationship of the weights. Use s to represent the weight of the square in grams and c to represent the weight of the circle in grams.

    b. One red circle weighs 12 grams. Write an inequality to represent the weight of one blue square.

    c. Could 0 be a value of s? Explain your reasoning.

3. a. Jada is taller than Diego. Diego is 54 inches tall (4 feet, 6 inches). Write an inequality that compares Jada's height in inches, j, to Diego's height.

    b. Jada is shorter than Elena. Elena is 5 feet tall. Write an inequality that compares Jada's height in inches, j, to Elena's height.

    (From Unit 7, Lesson 8.)

iM KH

4. Tyler has more than $10. Elena has more money than Tyler. Mai has more money than Elena. Let t be the amount of money that Tyler has, let e be the amount of money that Elena has, and let m be the amount of money that Mai has. Select **all** statements that are true:

A. $t < j$

B. $m > 10$

C. $e > 10$

D. $t > 10$

E. $e > m$

F. $t < e$

5. Which is greater, $\frac{-9}{20}$ or -0.5? Explain how you know. If you get stuck, consider plotting the numbers on a number line.

(From Unit 7, Lesson 3.)

6. Select **all** the expressions that are equivalent to $\left(\frac{1}{2}\right)^3$.

A. $\frac{1}{2} \cdot \frac{1}{2} \cdot \frac{1}{2}$

B. $\frac{1}{2^3}$

C. $\left(\frac{1}{3}\right)^2$

D. $\frac{1}{6}$

E. $\frac{1}{8}$

(From Unit 6, Lesson 13.)

Lesson 11: Points on the Coordinate Plane

Let's explore and extend the coordinate plane.

11.1: Guess My Line

1. Choose a horizontal or a vertical line on the grid. Draw 4 points on the line and label each point with its coordinates.

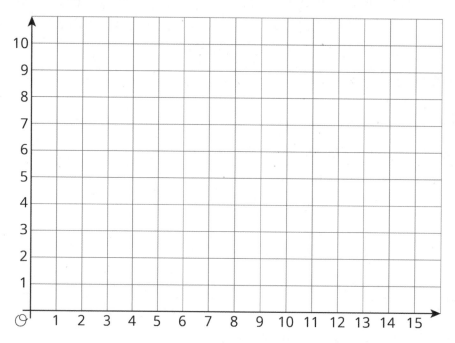

2. Tell your partner whether your line is horizontal or vertical, and have your partner guess the locations of your points by naming coordinates.

   If a guess is correct, put an X through the point. If your partner guessed a point that is on your line but not the point that you plotted, say, "That point is on my line, but is not one of my points."

   Take turns guessing each other's points, 3 guesses per turn.

11.2: The Coordinate Plane

1. Label each point on the coordinate plane with an ordered pair.

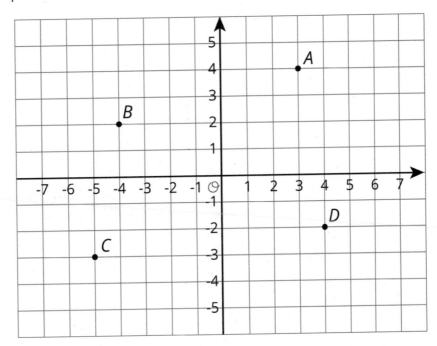

2. What do you notice about the locations and ordered pairs of B, C, and D? How are they different from those for point A?

3. Plot a point at (-2, 5). Label it E. Plot another point at (3, -4.5). Label it F.

4. The coordinate plane is divided into four **quadrants**, I, II, III, and IV, as shown here.

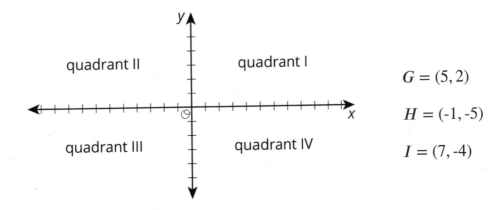

5. In which quadrant is point G located? Point H? Point I?

6. A point has a positive *y*-coordinate. In which quadrant could it be?

11.3: Coordinated Archery

Here is an image of an archery target on a coordinate plane. The scores for landing an arrow in the colored regions are shown.

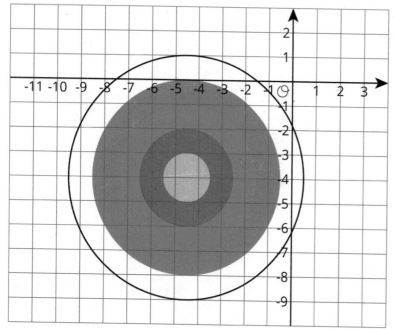

- Yellow: 10 points
- Red: 8 points
- Blue: 6 points
- Green: 4 points
- White: 2 points

Name the coordinates for a possible landing point to score:

1. 6 points

2. 10 points

3. 2 points

4. No points

5. 4 points

6. 8 points

iM KH

Are you ready for more?

Pretend you are stuck in a coordinate plane. You can only take vertical and horizontal steps that are one unit long.

1. How many ways are there to get from the point $(-3, 2)$ to $(-1, -1)$ if you will only step down and to the right?

2. How many ways are there to get from the point $(-1, -2)$ to $(4, 0)$ if you can only step up and to the right?

3. Make up some more problems like this and see what patterns you notice.

Lesson 11 Summary

Just as the number line can be extended to the left to include negative numbers, the x- and y-axis of a coordinate plane can also be extended to include negative values.

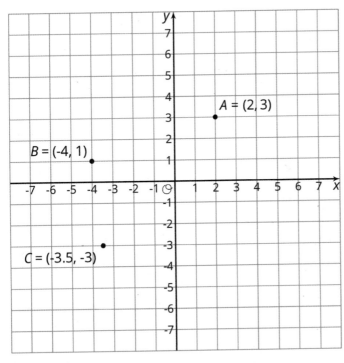

The ordered pair (x, y) can have negative x- and y-values. For $B = (-4, 1)$, the x-value of -4 tells us that the point is 4 units to the left of the y-axis. The y-value of 1 tells us that the point is one unit above the x-axis.

The same reasoning applies to the points A and C. The x- and y-coordinates for point A are positive, so A is to the right of the y-axis and above the x-axis. The x- and y-coordinates for point C are negative, so C is to the left of the y-axis and below the x-axis.

Glossary

- quadrant

Lesson 11 Practice Problems

1.   a. Graph these points in the coordinate plane: (-2, 3), (2, 3), (-2, -3), (2, -3).

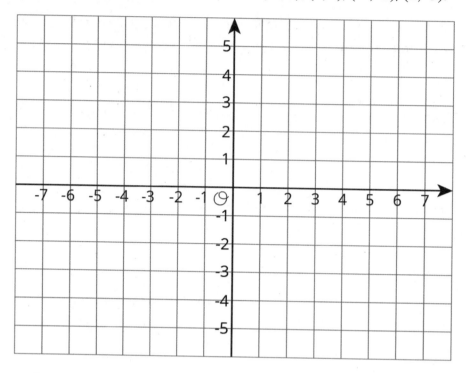

    b. Connect all of the points. Describe the figure.

2. Write the coordinates of each point.

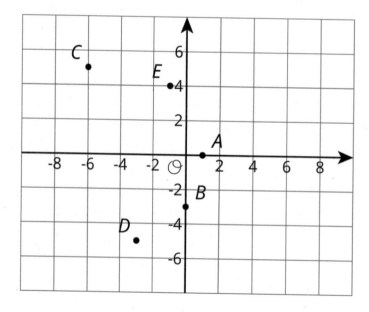

3. These three points form a horizontal line: $(-3.5, 4)$, $(0, 4)$, and $(6.2, 4)$. Name two additional points that fall on this line.

4. One night, it is 24°C warmer in Tucson than it was in Minneapolis. If the temperatures in Tucson and Minneapolis are opposites, what is the temperature in Tucson?

   A. -24°C

   B. -12°C

   C. 12°C

   D. 24°C

   (From Unit 7, Lesson 2.)

5. Lin ran 29 meters in 10 seconds. She ran at a constant speed.

   a. How far did Lin run every second?

   b. At this rate, how far can she run in 1 minute?

   (From Unit 2, Lesson 9.)

6. Noah is helping his band sell boxes of chocolate to fund a field trip. Each box contains 20 bars and each bar sells for $1.50.

    a. Complete the table for values of m.

boxes sold (b)	money collected (m)
1	
2	
3	
4	
5	
6	
7	
8	

    b. Write an equation for the amount of money, m, that will be collected if b boxes of chocolate bars are sold. Which is the independent variable and which is the dependent variable in your equation?

    c. Write an equation for the number of boxes, b, that were sold if m dollars were collected. Which is the independent variable and which is the dependent variable in your equation?

(From Unit 6, Lesson 16.)

iM KH

Lesson 12: Constructing the Coordinate Plane

Let's investigate different ways of creating a coordinate plane.

12.1: English Winter

The following data were collected over one December afternoon in England.

time after noon (hours)	temperature (°C)
0	5
1	3
2	4
3	2
4	1
5	-2
6	-3
7	-4
8	-4

A

B

C

1. Which set of axes would you choose to represent these data? Explain your reasoning.

2. Explain why the other two sets of axes did not seem as appropriate as the one you chose.

12.2: Axes Drawing Decisions

1. Here are three sets of coordinates. For each set, draw and label an appropriate pair of axes and plot the points.

   a. (1, 2), (3, -4), (-5, -2), (0, 2.5)

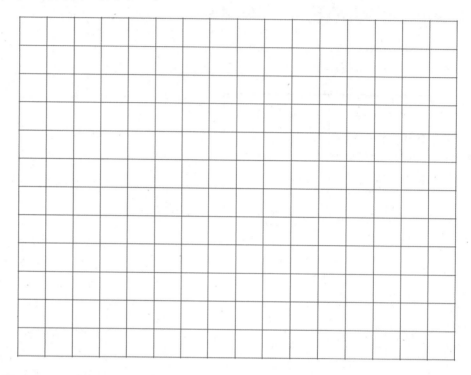

   b. (50, 50), (0, 0), (-10, -30), (-35, 40)

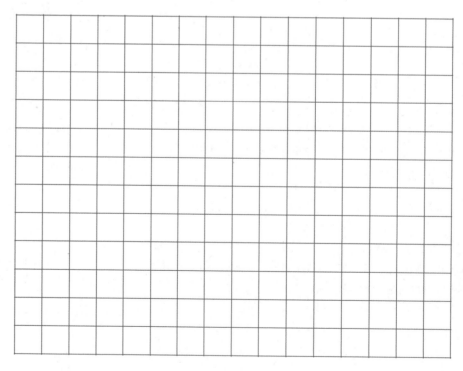

iM KH

c. $\left(\frac{1}{4}, \frac{3}{4}\right), \left(\frac{-5}{4}, \frac{1}{2}\right), \left(-1\frac{1}{4}, \frac{-3}{4}\right), \left(\frac{1}{4}, \frac{-1}{2}\right)$

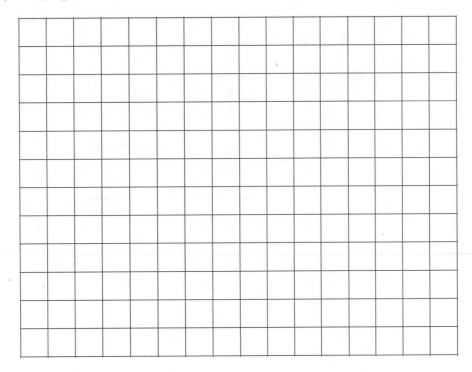

2. Discuss with a partner:

   ○ How are the axes and labels of your three drawings different?

   ○ How did the coordinates affect the way you drew the axes and label the numbers?

12.3: Positively A-maze-ing

Here is a maze on a coordinate plane. The black point in the center is (0, 0). The side of each grid square is 2 units long.

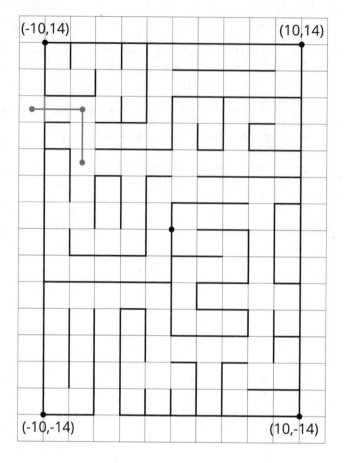

1. Enter the above maze at the location marked with a green segment. Draw line segments to show your way through and out of the maze. Label each turning point with a letter. Then, list all the letters and write their coordinates.

2. Choose any 2 turning points that share the same line segment. What is the same about their coordinates? Explain why they share that feature.

iM KH

Are you ready for more?

To get from the point $(2, 1)$ to $(-4, 3)$ you can go two units up and six units to the left, for a total distance of eight units. This is called the "taxicab distance," because a taxi driver would have to drive eight blocks to get between those two points on a map.

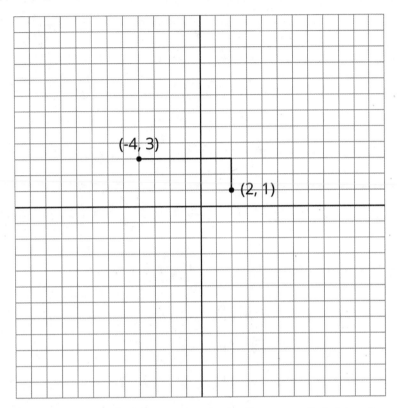

Find as many points as you can that have a taxicab distance of eight units away from $(2, 1)$. What shape do these points make?

Lesson 12 Summary

The coordinate plane can be used to show information involving pairs of numbers.

When using the coordinate plane, we should pay close attention to what each axis represents and what scale each uses.

Suppose we want to plot the following data about the temperatures in Minneapolis one evening.

time (hours from midnight)	temperature (degrees C)
-4	3
-1	-2
0	-4
3	-8

We can decide that the x-axis represents number of hours in relation to midnight and the y-axis represents temperatures in degrees Celsius.

- In this case, x-values less than 0 represent hours before midnight, and x-values greater than 0 represent hours after midnight.

- On the y-axis, the values represents temperatures above and below the freezing point of 0 degrees Celsius.

The data involve whole numbers, so it is appropriate that the each square on the grid represents a whole number.

- On the left of the origin, the x-axis needs to go as far as -4 or less (farther to the left). On the right, it needs to go to 3 or greater.

- Below the origin, the y-axis has to go as far as -8 or lower. Above the origin, it needs to go to 3 or higher.

Here is a graph of the data with the axes labeled appropriately.

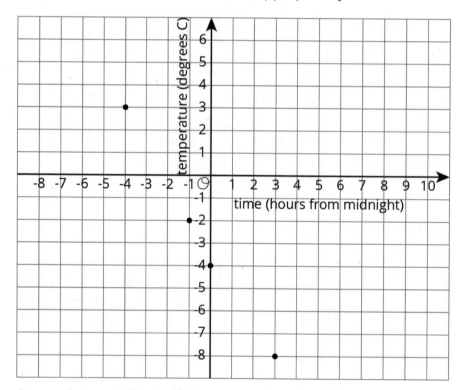

On this coordinate plane, a point at $(0, 0)$ would mean a temperature of 0 degrees Celsius at midnight. The point at $(-4, 3)$ means a temperature of 3 degrees Celsius at 4 hours before midnight (or 8 p.m.).

Lesson 12 Practice Problems

1. Draw and label an appropriate pair of axes and plot the points.

   $(\frac{1}{5}, \frac{4}{5})$

   $(-\frac{3}{5}, \frac{2}{5})$

   $(-1\frac{1}{5}, -\frac{4}{5})$

   $(\frac{1}{5}, -\frac{3}{5})$

2. Diego was asked to plot these points: $(-50, 0)$, $(150, 100)$, $(200, -100)$, $(350, 50)$, $(-250, 0)$. What interval could he use for each axis? Explain your reasoning.

3.   a. Name 4 points that would form a square with the origin at its center.

       b. Graph these points to check if they form a square.

4. Which of the following changes would you represent using a negative number? Explain what a positive number would represent in that situation.

   a. A loss of 4 points

   b. A gain of 50 yards

   c. A loss of $10

   d. An elevation above sea level

(From Unit 7, Lesson 5.)

5. Jada is buying notebooks for school. The cost of each notebook is $1.75.

   a. Write an equation that shows the cost of Jada's notebooks, c, in terms of the number of notebooks, n, that she buys.

   b. Which of the following could be points on the graph of your equation?

   $(1.75, 1)$ $(2, 3.50)$ $(5, 8.75)$ $(17.50, 10)$ $(9, 15.35)$

(From Unit 6, Lesson 16.)

6. A corn field has an area of 28.6 acres. It requires about 15,000,000 gallons of water. About how many gallons of water per acre is that?

   A. 5,000

   B. 50,000

   C. 500,000

   D. 5,000,000

(From Unit 5, Lesson 13.)

iM KH

Lesson 13: Interpreting Points on a Coordinate Plane

Let's examine what points on the coordinate plane can tell us.

13.1: Unlabeled Points

Label each point on the coordinate plane with the appropriate letter and ordered pair.

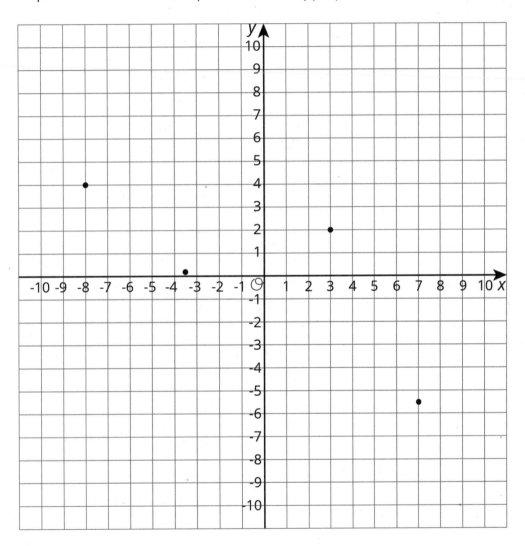

$A = (7, -5.5)$ $B = (-8, 4)$ $C = (3, 2)$ $D = (-3.5, 0.2)$

13.2: Account Balance

The graph shows the balance in a bank account over a period of 14 days. The axis labeled *b* represents account balance in dollars. The axis labeled *d* represents the day.

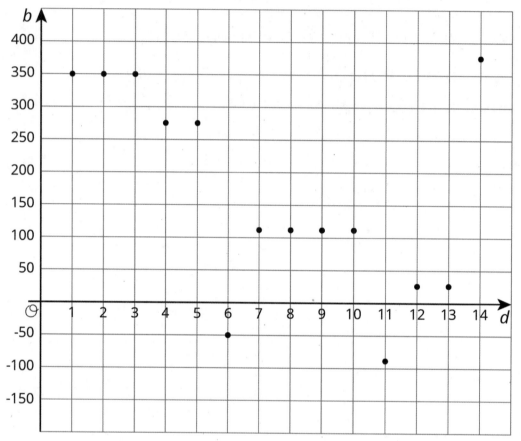

1. Estimate the greatest account balance. On which day did it occur?

2. Estimate the least account balance. On which day did it occur?

3. What does the point (6, -50) tell you about the account balance?

4. How can we interpret |-50| in the context?

13.3: High and Low Temperatures

The coordinate plane shows the high and low temperatures in Nome, Alaska over a period of 8 days. The axis labeled T represents temperatures in degrees Fahrenheit. The axis labeled d represents the day.

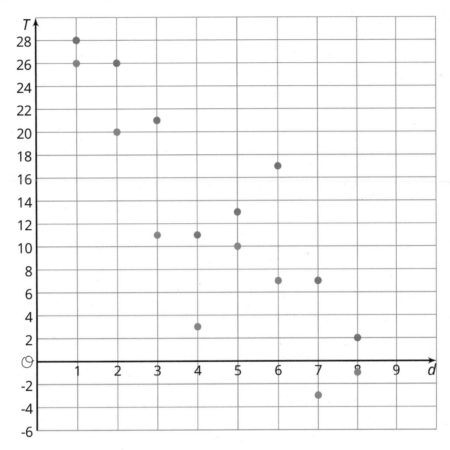

1. a. What was the warmest high temperature?

   b. Write an inequality to describe the high temperatures, H, over the 8-day period.

2. a. What was the coldest low temperature?

   b. Write an inequality to describe the low temperatures, L, over the 8-day period.

3. a. On which day(s) did the *largest* difference between the high and low temperatures occur? Write down this difference.

   b. On which day(s) did the *smallest* difference between the high and low temperatures occur? Write down this difference.

Are you ready for more?

Before doing this problem, do the problem about taxicab distance in an earlier lesson.

The point (0, 3) is 4 taxicab units away from (-4, 3) and 4 taxicab units away from (2, 1).

1. Find as many other points as you can that are 4 taxicab units away from *both* (-4, 3) and (2, 1).

2. Are there any points that are 3 taxicab units away from both points?

Lesson 13 Summary

Points on the coordinate plane can give us information about a context or a situation. One of those contexts is about money.

To open a bank account, we have to put money into the account. The account balance is the amount of money in the account at any given time. If we put in $350 when opening the account, then the account balance will be 350.

Sometimes we may have no money in the account and need to borrow money from the bank. In that situation, the account balance would have a negative value. If we borrow $200, then the account balance is -200.

A coordinate grid can be used to display both the balance and the day or time for any balance. This allows to see how the balance changes over time or to compare the balances of different days.

Similarly, if we plot on the coordinate plane data such as temperature over time, we can see how temperature changes over time or compare temperatures of different times.

Lesson 13 Practice Problems

1. The elevation of a submarine is shown in the table. Draw and label coordinate axes with an appropriate scale and plot the points.

time after noon (hours)	elevation (meters)
0	-567
1	-892
2	-1,606
3	-1,289
4	-990
5	-702
6	-365

2. The inequalities $h > 42$ and $h < 60$ represent the height requirements for an amusement park ride, where h represents a person's height in inches.

   Write a sentence or draw a sign that describes these rules as clearly as possible.

   (From Unit 7, Lesson 8.)

3. The x-axis represents the number of hours before or after noon, and the y-axis represents the temperature in degrees Celsius.

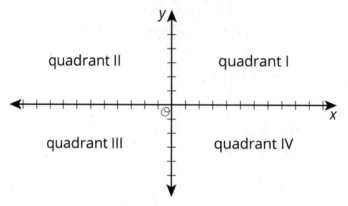

a. At 9 a.m., it was below freezing. In what quadrant would this point be plotted?

b. At 11 a.m., it was $10°C$. In what quadrant would this point be plotted?

c. Choose another time and temperature. Then tell the quadrant where the point should be plotted.

d. What does the point $(0, 0)$ represent in this context?

4. Solve each equation.

$3a = 12$ $b + 3.3 = 8.9$ $1 = \frac{1}{4}c$

$5\frac{1}{2} = d + \frac{1}{4}$ $2e = 6.4$

(From Unit 6, Lesson 4.)

iM KH

Lesson 14: Distances on a Coordinate Plane

Let's explore distance on the coordinate plane.

14.1: Coordinate Patterns

Plot points in your assigned quadrant and label them with their coordinates.

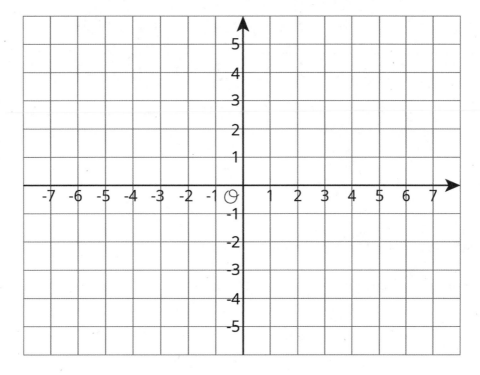

14.2: Signs of Numbers in Coordinates

1. Write the coordinates of each point.

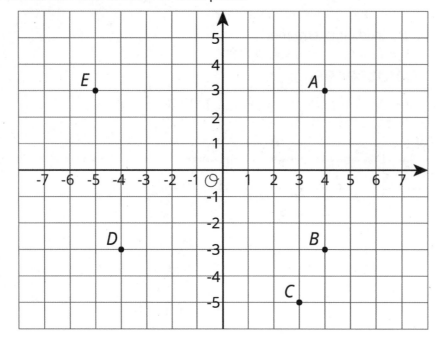

$A =$

$B =$

$C =$

$D =$

$E =$

2. Answer these questions for each pair of points.

   ○ How are the coordinates the same? How are they different?
   ○ How far away are they from the y-axis? To the left or to the right of it?
   ○ How far away are they from the x-axis? Above or below it?

   a. *A* and *B*

   b. *B* and *D*

   c. *A* and *D*

   Pause here for a class discussion.

iM KH

3. Point F has the same coordinates as point C, except its y-coordinate has the opposite sign.

    a. Plot point F on the coordinate plane and label it with its coordinates.

    b. How far away are F and C from the x-axis?

    c. What is the distance between F and C?

4. Point G has the same coordinates as point E, except its x-coordinate has the opposite sign.

    a. Plot point G on the coordinate plane and label it with its coordinates.

    b. How far away are G and E from the y-axis?

    c. What is the distance between G and E?

5. Point H has the same coordinates as point B, except its *both* coordinates have the opposite sign. In which quadrant is point H?

14.3: Finding Distances on a Coordinate Plane

1. Label each point with its coordinates.

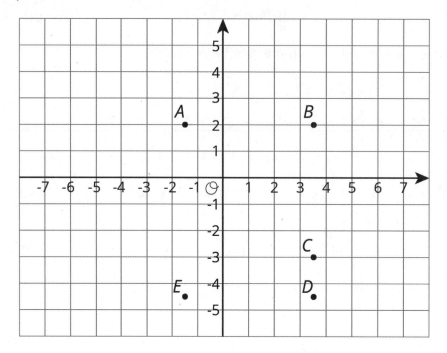

2. Find the distance between each of the following pairs of points.

    a. Point B and C

    b. Point D and B

    c. Point D and E

3. Which of the points are 5 units from (-1.5, -3)?

4. Which of the points are 2 units from (0.5, -4.5)?

5. Plot a point that is both 2.5 units from A and 9 units from E. Label that point M and write down its coordinates.

iM KH

Are you ready for more?

Priya says, "There are exactly four points that are 3 units away from (-5, 0)." Lin says, "I think there are a whole bunch of points that are 3 units away from (-5, 0)."

Do you agree with either of them? Explain your reasoning.

Lesson 14 Summary

The points $A = (5, 2)$, $B = (-5, 2)$, $C = (-5, -2)$, and $D = (5, -2)$ are shown in the plane. Notice that they all have almost the same coordinates, except the signs are different. They are all the same distance from each axis but are in different quadrants.

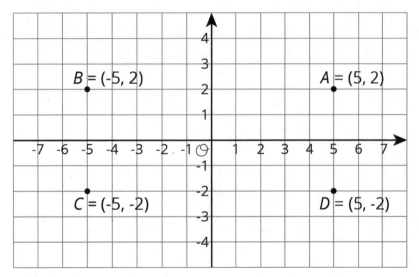

Notice that the vertical distance between points A and D is 4 units, because point A is 2 units above the horizontal axis and point D is 2 units below the horizontal axis. The horizontal distance between points A and B is 10 units, because point B is 5 units to the left of the vertical axis and point A is 5 units to the right of the vertical axis.

We can always tell which quadrant a point is located in by the signs of its coordinates.

x	y	quadrant
positive	positive	I
negative	positive	II
negative	negative	III
positive	negative	IV

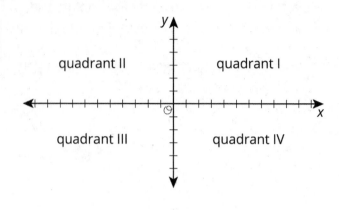

In general:

- If two points have x-coordinates that are opposites (like 5 and -5), they are the same distance away from the vertical axis, but one is to the left and the other to the right.

- If two points have y-coordinates that are opposites (like 2 and -2), they are the same distance away from the horizontal axis, but one is above and the other below.

When two points have the same value for the first or second coordinate, we can find the distance between them by subtracting the coordinates that are different. For example, consider $(1, 3)$ and $(5, 3)$:

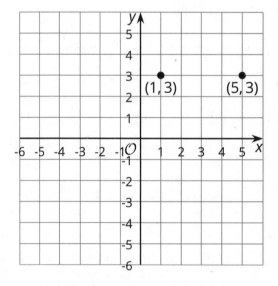

They have the same y-coordinate. If we subtract the x-coordinates, we get $5 - 1 = 4$. These points are 4 units apart.

iM KH

Lesson 14 Practice Problems

1. Here are 4 points on a coordinate plane.

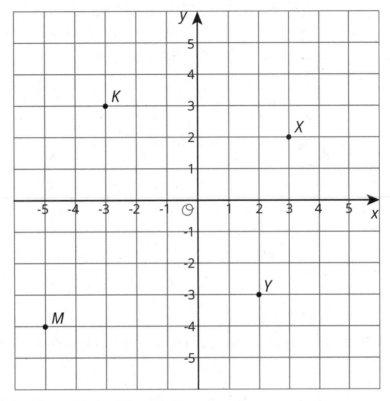

a. Label each point with its coordinates.

b. Plot a point that is 3 units from point K. Label it P.

c. Plot a point that is 2 units from point M. Label it W.

2. Each set of points are connected to form a line segment. What is the length of each?

a. A = $(3, 5)$ and B = $(3, 6)$

b. C = (-2, -3) and D = (-2, -6)

c. E = (-3, 1) and F = (-3, -1)

3. On the coordinate plane, plot four points that are each 3 units away from point $P = (-2, -1)$. Write the coordinates of each point.

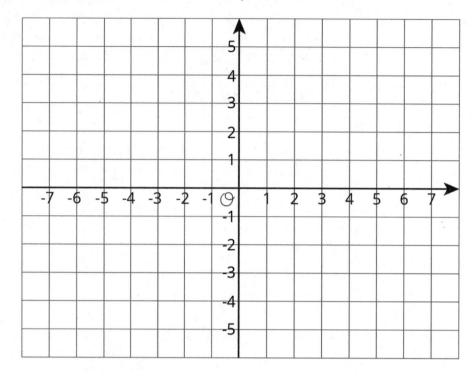

4. Noah's recipe for sparkling orange juice uses 4 liters of orange juice and 5 liters of soda water.

   a. Noah prepares large batches of sparkling orange juice for school parties. He usually knows the total number of liters, t, that he needs to prepare. Write an equation that shows how Noah can find s, the number of liters of soda water, if he knows t.

   b. Sometimes the school purchases a certain number, j, of liters of orange juice and Noah needs to figure out how much sparkling orange juice he can make. Write an equation that Noah can use to find t if he knows j.

   (From Unit 6, Lesson 16.)

5. For a suitcase to be checked on a flight (instead of carried by hand), it can weigh at most 50 pounds. Andre's suitcase weighs 23 kilograms. Can Andre check his suitcase? Explain or show your reasoning. (Note: 10 kilograms ≈ 22 pounds)

   (From Unit 3, Lesson 4.)

iM KH

Lesson 15: Shapes on the Coordinate Plane

Let's use the coordinate plane to solve problems and puzzles.

15.1: Figuring Out The Coordinate Plane

1. Draw a figure in the coordinate plane with at least three of following properties:

   ○ 6 vertices

   ○ Exactly 1 pair of parallel sides

   ○ At least 1 right angle

   ○ 2 sides with the same length

2. Is your figure a polygon? Explain how you know.

15.2: Plotting Polygons

Here are the coordinates for four polygons. Plot them on the coordinate plane, connect the points in the order that they are listed, and label each polygon with its letter name.

1. Polygon A: (-7, 4), (-8, 5), (-8, 6), (-7, 7), (-5, 7), (-5, 5), (-7, 4)

2. Polygon B: (4, 3), (3, 3), (2, 2), (2, 1), (3, 0), (4, 0), (5, 1), (5, 2), (4, 3)

3. Polygon C: (-8, -5), (-8, -8), (-5, -8), (-5, -5), (-8, -5)

4. Polygon D: (-5, 1), (-3, -3), (-1, -2), (0, 3), (-3, 3), (-5, 1)

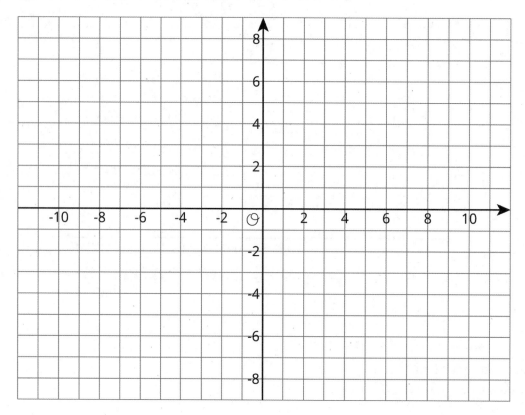

Are you ready for more?

Find the area of Polygon D in this activity.

iM KH

15.3: Four Quadrants of A-Maze-ing

1. The following diagram shows Andre's route through a maze. He started from the lower right entrance.

a. What are the coordinates of the first two and the last two points of his route?

b. How far did he walk from his starting point to his ending point? Show how you know.

2. Jada went into the maze and stopped at (-7, 2).

   a. Plot that point and other points that would lead her out of the maze (through the exit on the upper left side).

   b. How far from (-7, 2) must she walk to exit the maze? Show how you know.

Lesson 15 Summary

We can use coordinates to find lengths of segments in the coordinate plane.

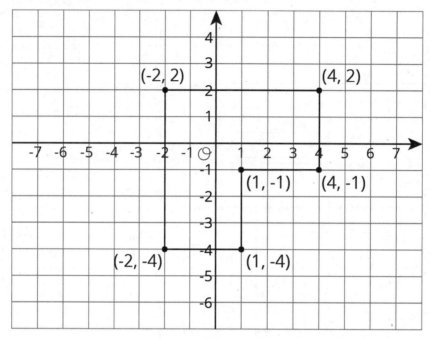

For example, we can find the perimeter of this polygon by finding the sum of its side lengths. Starting from (-2, 2) and moving clockwise, we can see that the lengths of the segments are 6, 3, 3, 3, 3, and 6 units. The perimeter is therefore 24 units.

In general:

- If two points have the same x-coordinate, they will be on the same vertical line, and we can find the distance between them.

- If two points have the same y-coordinate, they will be on the same horizontal line, and we can find the distance between them.

iM KH

Lesson 15 Practice Problems

1. The coordinates of a rectangle are $(3, 0)$, $(3, -5)$, $(-4, 0)$ and $(-4, -5)$

    a. What is the length and width of this rectangle?

    b. What is the perimeter of the rectangle?

    c. What is the area of the rectangle?

2. Draw a square with one vertex on the point $(-3, 5)$ and a perimeter of 20 units. Write the coordinates of each other vertex.

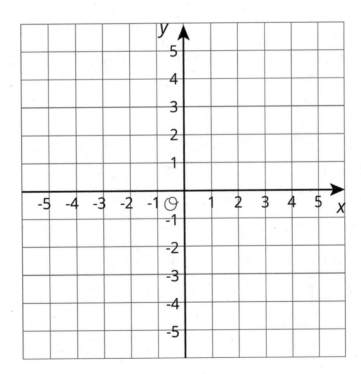

3. a. Plot and connect the following points to form a polygon.
   $(-3, 2), (2, 2), (2, -4), (-1, -4), (-1, -2), (-3, -2), (-3, 2)$

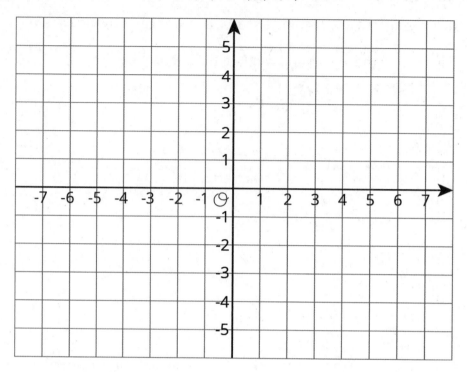

   b. Find the perimeter of the polygon.

4. For each situation, select **all** the equations that represent it. Choose one equation and solve it.

   a. Jada's cat weighs 3.45 kg. Andre's cat weighs 1.2 kg more than Jada's cat. How much does Andre's cat weigh?

   $x = 3.45 + 1.2$ $\qquad$ $x = 3.45 - 1.2$ $\qquad$ $x + 1.2 = 3.45$ $\qquad$ $x - 1.2 = 3.45$

   b. Apples cost $1.60 per pound at the farmer's market. They cost 1.5 times as much at the grocery store. How much do the apples cost per pound at the grocery store?

   $y = (1.5) \cdot (1.60)$ $\qquad$ $y = 1.60 \div 1.5$ $\qquad$ $(1.5)y = 1.60$ $\qquad$ $\frac{y}{1.5} = 1.60$

   (From Unit 6, Lesson 4.)

iM KH

Lesson 16: Common Factors

Let's use factors to solve problems.

16.1: Figures Made of Squares

How are the pairs of figures alike? How are they different?

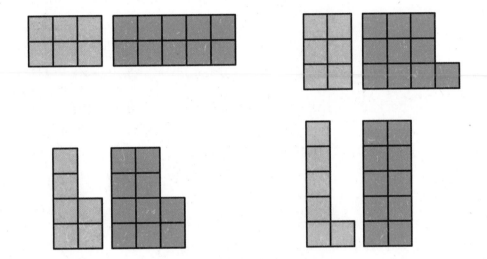

16.2: Diego's Bake Sale

Diego is preparing brownies and cookies for a bake sale. He would like to make equal-size bags for selling all of the 48 brownies and 64 cookies that he has. Organize your answer to each question so that it can be followed by others.

1. How can Diego package all the 48 brownies so that each bag has the same number of them? How many bags can he make, and how many brownies will be in each bag? Find all the possible ways to package the brownies.

2. How can Diego package all the 64 cookies so that each bag has the same number of them? How many bags can he make, and how many cookies will be in each bag? Find all the possible ways to package the cookies.

3. How can Diego package all the 48 brownies and 64 cookies so that each bag has the same combination of items? How many bags can he make, and how many of each will be in each bag? Find all the possible ways to package both items.

4. What is the largest number of combination bags that Diego can make with no left over? Explain to your partner how you know that it is the largest possible number of bags.

16.3: Greatest Common Factor

1. The **greatest common factor** of 30 and 18 is 6. What do you think the term "greatest common factor" means?

2. Find all of the **factors** of 21 and 6. Then, identify the greatest common factor of 21 and 6.

3. Find all of the factors of 28 and 12. Then, identify the greatest common factor of 28 and 12.

4. A rectangular bulletin board is 12 inches tall and 27 inches wide. Elena plans to cover it with squares of colored paper that are all the same size. The paper squares come in different sizes; all of them have whole-number inches for their side lengths.

    a. What is the side length of the largest square that Elena could use to cover the bulletin board completely without gaps and overlaps? Explain or show your reasoning.

    b. How is the solution to this problem related to greatest common factor?

Are you ready for more?

A school has 1,000 lockers, all lined up in a hallway. Each locker is closed. Then . . .

- One student goes down the hall and opens each locker.
- A second student goes down the hall and closes every second locker: lockers 2, 4, 6, and so on.
- A third student goes down the hall and changes every third locker. If a locker is open, he closes it. If a locker is closed, he opens it.
- A fourth student goes down the hall and changes every fourth locker.

This process continues up to the thousandth student! At the end of the process, which lockers will be open? (Hint: you may want to try this problem with a smaller number of lockers first.)

Lesson 16 Summary

A factor of a whole number n is a whole number that divides n evenly without a remainder. For example, 1, 2, 3, 4, 6, and 12 are all factors of 12 because each of them divides 12 evenly and without a remainder.

A **common factor** of two whole numbers is a factor that they have in common. For example, 1, 3, 5, and 15 are factors of 45; they are also factors of 60. We call 1, 3, 5, and 15 common factors of 45 and 60.

The **greatest common factor** (sometimes written as GCF) of two whole numbers is the greatest of all of the common factors. For example, 15 is the greatest common factor for 45 and 60.

One way to find the greatest common factor of two whole numbers is to list all of the factors for each, and then look for the greatest factor they have in common. Let's try to find the greatest common factor of 18 and 24. First, we list all the factors of each number.

- Factors of 18: **1**, **2**, **3**, **6**, 9,18

- Factors of 24: **1**, **2**, **3**, 4, **6**, 8, 12, 24

The common factors are 1, 2, 3, and 6. Of these, 6 is the greatest one, so 6 is the greatest common factor of 18 and 24.

Glossary

- common factor
- greatest common factor

Lesson 16 Practice Problems

1. A teacher is making gift bags. Each bag is to be filled with pencils and stickers. The teacher has 24 pencils and 36 stickers to use. Each bag will have the same number of each item, with no items left over. For example, she could make 2 bags with 12 pencils and 18 stickers each.

   What are the other possibilities? Explain or show your reasoning.

2.   a. List all the factors of 42.

   b. What is the greatest common factor of 42 and 15?

   c. What is the greatest common factor of 42 and 50?

3. A school chorus has 90 sixth-grade students and 75 seventh-grade students. The music director wants to make groups of performers, with the same combination of sixth- and seventh-grade students in each group. She wants to form as many groups as possible.

   a. What is the largest number of groups that could be formed? Explain or show your reasoning.

   b. If that many groups are formed, how many students of each grade level would be in each group?

4. Here are some bank transactions from a bank account last week. Which transactions represent negative values?

   Monday: $650 paycheck deposited

   Tuesday: $40 withdrawal from the ATM at the gas pump

   Wednesday: $20 credit for returned merchandise

   Thursday: $125 deducted for cell phone charges

   Friday: $45 check written to pay for book order

   Saturday: $80 withdrawal for weekend spending money

   Sunday: $10 cash-back reward deposited from a credit card company

   (From Unit 7, Lesson 13.)

5. Find the quotients.

   a. $\frac{1}{7} \div \frac{1}{8}$

   b. $\frac{12}{5} \div \frac{6}{5}$

   c. $\frac{1}{10} \div 10$

   d. $\frac{9}{10} \div \frac{10}{9}$

   (From Unit 4, Lesson 11.)

6. An elephant can travel at a constant speed of 25 miles per hour, while a giraffe can travel at a constant speed of 16 miles in $\frac{1}{2}$ hour.

   a. Which animal runs faster? Explain your reasoning.

   b. How far can each animal run in 3 hours?

   (From Unit 2, Lesson 9.)

Lesson 17: Common Multiples

Let's use multiples to solve problems.

17.1: Notice and Wonder: Multiples

Circle all the multiples of 4 in this list.

1 2 3 4 5 6 7 8 9 10 11 12 13 14 15 16 17 18 19 20 21 22 23 24 25 26

Circle all the multiples of 6 in this list.

1 2 3 4 5 6 7 8 9 10 11 12 13 14 15 16 17 18 19 20 21 22 23 24 25 26

What do you notice? What do you wonder?

17.2: The Florist's Order

A florist can order roses in bunches of 12 and lilies in bunches of 8. Last month she ordered the same number of roses and lilies.

1. If she ordered no more than 100 of each kind of flower, how many bunches of each could she have ordered? Find all the possible combinations.

2. What is the smallest number of bunches of roses that she could have ordered? What about the smallest number of bunches of lilies? Explain your reasoning.

iM KH

17.3: Least Common Multiple

The **least common multiple** of 6 and 8 is 24.

1. What do you think the term "least common multiple" means?

2. Find all of the **multiples** of 10 and 8 that are less than 100. Find the least common multiple of 10 and 8.

3. Find all of the multiples of 7 and 9 that are less than 100. Find the least common multiple of 7 and 9.

Are you ready for more?

1. What is the least common multiple of 10 and 20?

2. What is the least common multiple of 4 and 24?

3. In the previous two questions, one number is a multiple of the other. What do you notice about their least common multiple? Do you think this will always happen when one number is a multiple of the other? Explain your reasoning.

17.4: Prizes on Grand Opening Day

Lin's uncle is opening a bakery. On the bakery's grand opening day, he plans to give away prizes to the first 50 customers that enter the shop. Every fifth customer will get a free bagel. Every ninth customer will get a free blueberry muffin. Every 12th customer will get a free slice of carrot cake.

1. Diego is waiting in line and is the 23rd customer. He thinks that he should get farther back in line in order to get a prize. Is he right? If so, how far back should he go to get at least one prize? Explain your reasoning.

2. Jada is the 36th customer.

   a. Will she get a prize? If so, what prize will she get?

   b. Is it possible for her to get more than one prize? How do you know? Explain your reasoning.

3. How many prizes total will Lin's uncle give away? Explain your reasoning.

Lesson 17 Summary

A multiple of a whole number is a product of that number with another whole number. For example, 20 is a multiple of 4 because $20 = 5 \cdot 4$.

A **common multiple** for two whole numbers is a number that is a multiple of both numbers. For example, 20 is a multiple of 2 and a multiple of 5, so 20 is a common multiple of 2 and 5.

The **least common multiple** (sometimes written as LCM) of two whole numbers is the smallest multiple they have in common. For example, 30 is the least common multiple of 6 and 10.

One way to find the least common multiple of two numbers is to list multiples of each in order until we find the smallest multiple they have in common. Let's find the least common multiple for 4 and 10. First, we list some multiples of each number.

- Multiples of 4: 4, 8, 12, 16, **20**, 24, 28, 32, 36, **40**, 44 . . .

- Multiples of 10: 10, **20**, 30, **40**, 50, . . .

20 and 40 are both common multiples of 4 and 10 (as are 60, 80, . . .), but 20 is the smallest number that is on *both* lists, so 20 is the least common multiple.

Glossary

- common multiple
- least common multiple

Lesson 17 Practice Problems

1.   a. A green light blinks every 4 seconds and a yellow light blinks every 5 seconds. When will both lights blink at the same time?

    b. A red light blinks every 12 seconds and a blue light blinks every 9 seconds. When will both lights blink at the same time?

    c. Explain how to determine when 2 lights blink together.

2.   a. List all multiples of 10 up to 100.

    b. List all multiples of 15 up to 100.

    c. What is the least common multiple of 10 and 15?

3. Cups are sold in packages of 8. Napkins are sold in packages of 12.

    a. What is the fewest number of packages of cups and the fewest number of packages of napkins that can be purchased so there will be the same number of cups as napkins?

    b. How many sets of cups and napkins will there be?

4. a. Plot and connect these points to form a polygon.

    $(-5, 3), (3, 3), (1, -2), (-3, -2)$

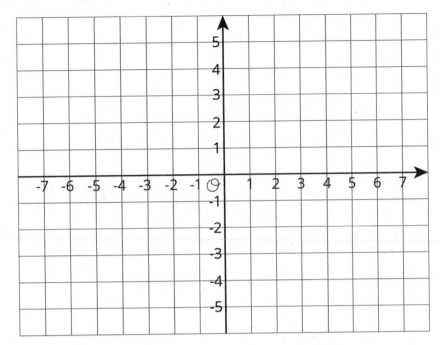

    b. Find the lengths of the two horizontal sides of the polygon.

(From Unit 7, Lesson 15.)

5. Rectangle ABCD is drawn on a coordinate plane. A = $(-6, 9)$ and B = $(5, 9)$. What could be the locations of points C and D?

(From Unit 7, Lesson 14.)

6. A school wants to raise $2,500 to support its music program.

    a. If it has met 20% of its goal so far, how much money has it raised?

    b. If it raises 175% of its goal, how much money will the music program receive? Show your reasoning.

(From Unit 3, Lesson 14.)

Lesson 18: Using Common Multiples and Common Factors

Let's use common factors and common multiple to solve problems.

18.1: Keeping a Steady Beat

Your teacher will give you instructions for playing a rhythm game. As you play the game, think about these questions:

- When will the two sounds happen at the same time?

- How does this game relate to common factors or common multiples?

18.2: Factors and Multiples

Work with your partner to solve the following problems.

1. **Party.** Elena is buying cups and plates for her party. Cups are sold in packs of 8 and plates are sold in packs of 6. She wants to have the same number of plates and cups.

   a. Find a number of plates and cups that meets her requirement.

   b. How many packs of each supply will she need to buy to get that number?

   c. Name two other quantities of plates and cups she could get to meet her requirement.

2. **Tiles**. A restaurant owner is replacing the restaurant's bathroom floor with square tiles. The tiles will be laid side-by-side to cover the entire bathroom with no gaps, and none of the tiles can be cut. The floor is a rectangle that measures 24 feet by 18 feet.

   a. What is the largest possible tile size she could use? Write the side length in feet. Explain how you know it's the largest possible tile.

   b. How many of these largest size tiles are needed?

   c. Name more tile sizes that are whole number of feet that she could use to cover the bathroom floor. Write the side lengths (in feet) of the square tiles.

3. **Stickers**. To celebrate the first day of spring, Lin is putting stickers on some of the 100 lockers along one side of her middle school's hallway. She puts a skateboard sticker on every 4th locker (starting with locker 4), and a kite sticker on every 5th locker (starting with locker 5).

   a. Name three lockers that will get both stickers.

   b. After Lin makes her way down the hall, will the 30th locker have no stickers, 1 sticker, or 2 stickers? Explain how you know.

4. **Kits.** The school nurse is assembling first-aid kits for the teachers. She has 75 bandages and 90 throat lozenges. All the kits must have the same number of each supply, and all supplies must be used.

   a. What is the largest number of kits the nurse can make?

   b. How many bandages and lozenges will be in each kit?

5. What kind of mathematical work was involved in each of the previous problems? Put a checkmark to show what the questions were about.

problem	finding multiples	finding least common multiple	finding factors	finding greatest common factor
Party				
Tiles				
Stickers				
Kits				

iM KH

Are you ready for more?

You probably know how to draw a five-pointed star without lifting your pencil. One way to do this is to start with five dots arranged in a circle, then connect every second dot.

If you try the same thing with six dots arranged in a circle, you will have to lift your pencil. Once you make the first triangle, you'll have to find an empty dot and start the process over. Your six-pointed star has two pieces that are each drawn without lifting the pencil.

With twelve dots arranged in a circle, we can make some twelve-pointed stars.

1. Start with one dot and connect every second dot, as if you were drawing a five-pointed star. Can you draw the twelve-pointed star without lifting your pencil? If not, how many pieces does the twelve-pointed star have?

2. This time, connect every third dot. Can you draw this twelve-pointed star without lifting your pencil? If not, how many pieces do you get?

3. What do you think will happen if you connect every
   fourth dot? Try it. How many pieces do you get?

4. Do you think there is any way to draw a twelve-pointed
   star without lifting your pencil? Try it out.

5. Now investigate eight-pointed stars, nine-pointed stars, and ten-pointed stars. What
   patterns do you notice?

iM KH

18.3: More Factors and Multiples

Here are five more problems. Read and discuss each one with your group. *Without solving,* predict whether each problem involves finding common multiples or finding common factors. Circle one or more options to show your prediction.

1. **Soccer.** Diego and Andre are both in a summer soccer league. During the month of August, Diego has a game every 3rd day, starting August 3rd, and Andre has a game every 4th day, starting August 4th.

   ○ common multiples   ○ common factors

   ○ least common multiple   ○ greatest common factor

   a. What is the first date that both boys will have a game?

   b. How many of their games fall on the same date?

2. **Performances.** During a performing arts festival, students from elementary and middle schools will be grouped together for various performances. There are 32 elementary students and 40 middle-school students. The arts director wants identical groups for the performances, with students from both schools in each group. Each student can be a part of only one group.

   ○ common multiples   ○ common factors

   ○ least common multiple   ○ greatest common factor

   a. Name all possible groupings.

   b. What is the largest number of groups that can be formed? How many elementary school students and how many middle school students will be in each group?

3. **Lights.** There is a string of holiday lights with red, gold, and blue lights. The red lights are set to blink every 12 seconds, the gold lights are set to blink every 8 seconds, and the blue lights are set to blink every 6 seconds. The lights are on an automatic timer that starts each day at 7:00 p.m. and stops at midnight.

     ○ common multiples   ○ common factors

     ○ least common multiple   ○ greatest common factor

a. After how much time with all 3 lights blink at the exact same time?

b. How many times total will this happen in one day?

4. **Banners.** Noah has two pieces of cloth. He is making square banners for students to hold during the opening day game. One piece of cloth is 72 inches wide. The other is 90 inches wide. He wants to use all the cloth, and each square banner must be of equal width and as wide as possible.

     ○ common multiples   ○ common factors

     ○ least common multiple   ○ greatest common factor

a. How wide should he cut the banners?

b. How many banners can he cut?

5. **Dancers.** At Elena's dance recital her performance begins with a line of 48 dancers that perform in the dark with a black light that illuminates white clothing. All 48 dancers enter the stage in a straight line. Every 3rd dancer wears a white headband, every 5th dancer wears a white belt, and every 9th dancer wears a set of white gloves.

     ○ common multiples   ○ common factors

     ○ least common multiple   ○ greatest common factor

a. If Elena is the 30th dancer, what accessories will she wear?

b. Will any of the dancers wear all 3 accessories? If so, which one(s)?

c. How many of each accessory will the dance teacher need to order?

iM KH

6. Your teacher will assign your group a problem. Work with your group to solve the problem. Show your reasoning. Pause here so your teacher can review your work.

7. Work with your group to create a visual display that includes a diagram, an equation, and a math vocabulary word that would help to explain your mathematical thinking while solving the problem.

8. Prepare a short presentation in which all group members are involved. Your presentation should include: the problem (read aloud), your group's prediction of what mathematical concept the problem involved, and an explanation of each step of the solving process.

18.4: Factors and Multiples Bingo

Your teacher will explain the directions for a bingo game. Here are some things to keep in mind:

- Share one bingo board and some bingo chips with a partner.

- To play the game, your teacher will read statements aloud. You may help one another decide what numbers fit each statement, but speak only in a whisper. If the teacher hears anything above a whisper, you are out.

- The first person to call bingo needs to call out each number and identify the statement that it corresponds to. If there is an error in identifying statements, that player is out and the round continues.

Good luck, and have fun!

Lesson 18 Summary

If a problem requires dividing two whole numbers by the same whole number, solving it involves looking for a common factor. If it requires finding the *largest* number that can divide into the two whole numbers, we are looking for the *greatest common factor*.

Suppose we have 12 bagels and 18 muffins and want to make bags so each bag has the same combination of bagels and muffins. The common factors of 12 and 18 tell us possible number of bags that can be made.

The common factors of 12 and 18 are 1, 2, 3, and 6. For these numbers of bags, here are the number of bagels and muffins per bag.

- 1 bag: 12 bagels and 18 muffins

- 2 bags: 6 bagels and 9 muffins

- 3 bags: 4 bagels and 6 muffins

- 6 bags: 2 bagels and 3 muffins

We can see that the largest number of bags that can be made, 6, is the greatest common factor.

If a problem requires finding a number that is a multiple of two given numbers, solving it involves looking for a common multiple. If it requires finding the *first* instance the two numbers share a multiple, we are looking for the *least common multiple*.

Suppose forks are sold in boxes of 9 and spoons are sold in boxes of 15, and we want to buy an equal number of each. The multiples of 9 tell us how many forks we could buy, and the multiples of 15 tell us how many spoons we could buy, as shown here.

- Forks: 9, 18, 27, 36, 45, 54, 63, 72, 90. . .

- Spoons: 15, 30, 45, 60, 75, 90. . .

If we want as many forks as spoons, our options are 45, 90, 135, and so on, but the smallest number of utensils we could buy is 45, the least common multiple. This means buying 5 boxes of forks ($5 \cdot 9 = 45$) and 3 boxes of spoons ($3 \cdot 15 = 45$).

iM KH

Lesson 18 Practice Problems

1. Mai, Clare, and Noah are making signs to advertise the school dance. It takes Mai 6 minutes to complete a sign, it takes Clare 8 minutes to complete a sign, and it takes Noah 5 minutes to complete a sign. They keep working at the same rate for a half hour.

   a. Will Mai and Clare complete a sign at the same time? Explain your reasoning.

   b. Will Mai and Noah complete a sign at the same time? Explain your reasoning.

   c. Will Clare and Noah complete a sign at the same time? Explain your reasoning

   d. Will all three students complete a sign at the same time? Explain your reasoning

2. Diego has 48 chocolate chip cookies, 64 vanilla cookies, and 100 raisin cookies for a bake sale. He wants to make bags that have all three cookie flavors and the same number of each flavor per bag.

   a. How many bags can he make without having any cookies left over?

   b. Find the another solution to this problem.

   (From Unit 7, Lesson 16.)

3. a. Find the product of 12 and 8.

    b. Find the greatest common factor of 12 and 8.

    c. Find the least common multiple of 12 and 8.

    d. Find the product of the greatest common factor and the least common multiple of 12 and 8.

    e. What do you notice about the answers to question 1 and question 4?

    f. Choose 2 other numbers and repeat the previous steps. Do you get the same results?

4. a. Given the point $(5.5, -7)$, name a second point so that the two points form a vertical segment. What is the length of the segment?

    b. Given the point $(3, 3.5)$, name a second point so that the two points form a horizontal segment. What is the length of the segment?

(From Unit 7, Lesson 11.)

5. Find the value of each expression mentally.

   a. $\frac{1}{2} \cdot 37 - \frac{1}{2} \cdot 7$

   b. $3.5 \cdot 40 + 3.5 \cdot 60$

   c. $999 \cdot 5$

(From Unit 6, Lesson 9.)

iM KH

Lesson 19: Drawing on the Coordinate Plane

- Let's draw on the coordinate plane.

19.1: Cat Pictures

Use graphing technology to recreate this image. If graphing technology is not available, list the ordered pairs that make up this image. Then compare your list with a partner.

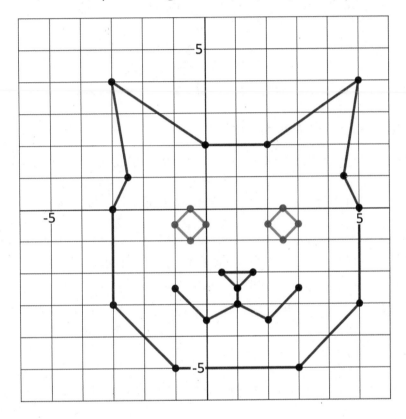

If you have time, consider adding more details to your image such as whiskers, the inside of the ears, a bow, or a body.

Are you ready for more?

If you are using graphing technology, add these statements to the list of things being graphed:

$$x > 6$$
$$y > 5$$
$$x < -4$$
$$y < -6$$

Describe the result. Why do you think that happened?

19.2: Design Your Own Image

Use graphing technology to create an image of your own design. You could draw a different animal, a vehicle, a building, or something else. Make sure your image includes at least 4 points in each quadrant of the coordinate plane.

If graphing technology is not available, create your image on graph paper, and then list the ordered pairs that make up your image. Trade lists with a partner but do not show them your image. Graph your partner's ordered pairs and see if your images match.

iM KH

Learning Targets

Lesson 1: Positive and Negative Numbers

- I can explain what 0, positive numbers, and negative numbers mean in the context of temperature and elevation.

- I can use positive and negative numbers to describe temperature and elevation.

- I know what positive and negative numbers are.

Lesson 2: Points on the Number Line

- I can determine or approximate the value of any point on a number line.

- I can represent negative numbers on a number line.

- I understand what it means for numbers to be opposites.

Lesson 3: Comparing Positive and Negative Numbers

- I can explain how to use the positions of numbers on a number line to compare them.

- I can explain what a rational number is.

- I can use inequalities to compare positive and negative numbers.

Lesson 4: Ordering Rational Numbers

- I can compare and order rational numbers.

- I can use phrases like "greater than," "less than," and "opposite" to compare rational numbers.

Lesson 5: Using Negative Numbers to Make Sense of Contexts

- I can explain and use negative numbers in situations involving money.

- I can interpret and use negative numbers in different contexts.

Lesson 6: Absolute Value of Numbers

- I can explain what the absolute value of a number is.

- I can find the absolute values of rational numbers.

- I can recognize and use the notation for absolute value.

Lesson 7: Comparing Numbers and Distance from Zero

- I can explain what absolute value means in situations involving elevation.

- I can use absolute values to describe elevations.

- I can use inequalities to compare rational numbers and the absolute values of rational numbers.

Lesson 8: Writing and Graphing Inequalities

- I can graph inequalities on a number line.

- I can write an inequality to represent a situation.

Lesson 9: Solutions of Inequalities

- I can determine if a particular number is a solution to an inequality.

- I can explain what it means for a number to be a solution to an inequality.

- I can graph the solutions to an inequality on a number line.

Lesson 10: Interpreting Inequalities

- I can explain what the solution to an inequality means in a situation.

- I can write inequalities that involves more than one variable.

Lesson 11: Points on the Coordinate Plane

- I can describe a coordinate plane that has four quadrants.

- I can plot points with negative coordinates in the coordinate plane.

- I know what negative numbers in coordinates tell us.

Lesson 12: Constructing the Coordinate Plane

- When given points to plot, I can construct a coordinate plane with an appropriate scale and pair of axes.

Lesson 13: Interpreting Points on a Coordinate Plane

- I can explain how rational numbers represent balances in a money context.

- I can explain what points in a four-quadrant coordinate plane represent in a situation.

- I can plot points in a four-quadrant coordinate plane to represent situations and solve problems.

Lesson 14: Distances on a Coordinate Plane

- I can find horizontal and vertical distances between points on the coordinate plane.

Lesson 15: Shapes on the Coordinate Plane

- I can find the lengths of horizontal and vertical segments in the coordinate plane.

- I can plot polygons on the coordinate plane when I have the coordinates for the vertices.

Lesson 16: Common Factors

- I can explain what a common factor is.

- I can explain what the greatest common factor is.

- I can find the greatest common factor of two whole numbers.

Lesson 17: Common Multiples

- I can explain what a common multiple is.

- I can explain what the least common multiple is.

- I can find the least common multiple of two whole numbers.

Lesson 18: Using Common Multiples and Common Factors

- I can solve problems using common factors and multiples.

Lesson 19: Drawing on the Coordinate Plane

- I can use ordered pairs to draw a picture.

GRADE 6

STUDENT EDITION
Book 3

Kendall Hunt |

Lesson 1: Got Data?

Let's explore different kinds of data.

1.1: Dots of Data

Here is a **dot plot** for a data set.

1. Determine if each of the following would be an appropriate label to represent the data in the dot plot? Be prepared to explain your reasoning.

   a. Number of children per class.

   b. Distance between home and school, in miles.

   c. Hours spent watching TV each day.

   d. Weight of elephants, in pounds.

   e. Points received on a homework assignment.

2. Think of another label that can be used with the dot plot.

   a. Write it below the scale of the dot plot. Be sure to include the unit of measurement.

   b. In your scenario, what does one dot represent?

   c. In your scenario, what would a data point of 0 mean? What would a data point of $3\frac{1}{4}$ mean?

iM KH

1.2: Surveying the Class

Here are some survey questions. Your teacher will explain which questions can be used to learn more about the students in your class and how the responses will be collected. The data that your class collects will be used in upcoming activities.

1. How long does it usually take you to travel to school? Answer to the nearest minute.

2. How do you travel to school on most days? Choose one.

   ○ Walk   ○ Car   ○ Public transport

   ○ Bike   ○ School bus   ○ Other

   ○ Scooter or skateboard

3. How tall are you without your shoes on? Answer to the nearest centimeter.

4. What is the length of your right foot without your shoe on? Answer to the nearest centimeter.

5. What is your arm span? Stretch your arms open, and measure the distance from the tip of your right hand's middle finger to the tip of your left hand's middle finger, across your back. Answer to the nearest centimeter.

6. How important are the following issues to you? Rate each on a scale from 0 (not important) to 10 (very important).

   a. Reducing pollution

   b. Recycling

   c. Conserving water

7. Do you have any siblings? _____ Yes _____ No

8. How many hours of sleep per night do you usually get when you have school the next day? Answer to the nearest half hour.

9. How many hours of sleep per night do you usually get when you do not have school the next day? Answer to the nearest half hour.

10. Other than traveling from school, what do you do right after school on most days?

- ○ Have a snack
- ○ Do homework
- ○ Read a book
- ○ Talk on the phone
- ○ Practice a sport
- ○ Do chores
- ○ Use the computer
- ○ Participate in an extracurricular activity

11. If you could meet one of these celebrities, who would you choose?

- ○ A city or state leader
- ○ A champion athlete
- ○ A movie star
- ○ A musical artist
- ○ A best-selling author

12. Estimate how much time per week you usually spend on each of these activities. Answer to the nearest quarter of an hour.

a. Playing sports or doing outdoor activities

b. Using a screen for fun (watching TV, playing computer games, etc.)

c. Doing homework

d. Reading

iM KH

1.3: Numerical and Categorical Data

The list of survey questions in the activity earlier can help you complete these exercises.

1. The first survey question about travel *time* produces **numerical data**. Identify two other questions that produce numerical data. For each, describe what was measured and its unit of measurement.

    a. Question #: _____   What was measured:

    Unit of measurement:

    b. Question #: _____   What was measured:

    Unit of measurement:

2. The second survey question about travel *method* produces **categorical data**. Identify two other questions that produce categorical data. For each, describe what characteristic or feature was being studied.

    a. Question #: _____   Characteristic being studied:

    b. Question #: _____   Characteristic being studied:

3. Think about the responses to these survey questions. Do they produce numerical or categorical data? Be prepared to explain how you know.

    a. How many pets do you have?

    b. How many years have you lived in this state?

    c. What is your favorite band?

    d. What kind of music do you like best?

    e. What is the area code of your school's phone number?

    f. Where were you born?

    g. How much does your backpack weigh?

4. Name two characteristics you could investigate to learn more about your classmates. Make sure one would give categorical data and the other would give numerical data.

Are you ready for more?

Priya and Han collected data on the birth months of students in their class. Here are the lists of their records for the same group of students.

This list shows Priya's records.

Jan	Apr	Jan	Feb	Oct	May	June	July
Aug	Aug	Sep	Jan	Feb	Mar	Apr	Nov
Nov	Dec	Feb	Mar				

This list shows Han's records.

1	4	1	2	10	5	6	7
8	8	9	1	2	3	4	11
11	12	2	3				

1. How are their records alike? How are they different?

2. What kind of data—categorical or numerical—do you think the variable "birth month" produces? Explain how you know.

Lesson 1 Summary

The table contains data about 10 dogs.

dog name	weight (kg)	breed
Duke	36	German shepherd
Coco	6	pug
Pierre	7	pug
Ginger	35	German shepherd
Lucky	10	beagle
Daisy	10	beagle
Buster	35	German shepherd
Pepper	7	pug
Rocky	7	beagle
Lady	32	German shepherd

- The weights of the dogs are an example of **numerical data**, which is data that are numbers, quantities, or measurements. The weights of the dogs are measurements in kilograms.

- The dog breeds are an example of **categorical data**, which is data containing values that can be sorted into categories. In this case, there are three categories for dog breeds: pug, beagle, and German shepherd.

Some data with numbers are categorical because the numbers are *not* quantities or measurements. For example, telephone area codes are categorical data, because the numbers are labels rather than quantities or measurements.

Numerical data can be represented with a **dot plot** (sometimes called a line plot). Here is a dot plot that shows the weights of the dogs.

dog weights in kilograms

We can collect and study both kinds of data by doing surveys or taking measurements. When we do, it is important to think about what feature we are studying (for example, breeds of dogs or weights of dogs) and what units of measurement are used.

Glossary

- categorical data
- dot plot
- numerical data

iM KH

Lesson 1 Practice Problems

1. Tyler asked 10 students at his school how much time in minutes it takes them to get from home to school. Determine if each of these dot plots could represent the data Tyler collected. Explain your reasoning for each dot plot.

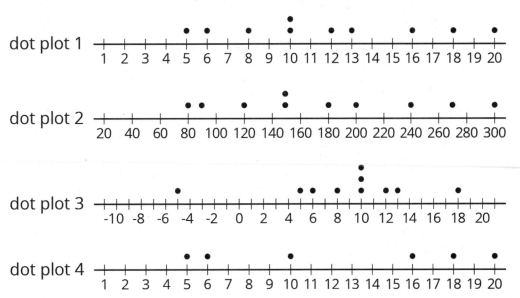

2. Here is a list of questions. For each question, decide if the responses will produce numerical data or categorical data and give two possible responses.

   a. What is your favorite breakfast food?

   b. How did you get to school this morning?

   c. How many different teachers do you have?

   d. What is the last thing you ate or drank?

   e. How many minutes did it take you to get ready this morning—from waking up to leaving for school?

3. a. Write two questions that you could ask the students in your class that would result in categorical data. For each question, explain how you know that responses to it would produce categorical data.

   b. Write two questions that you could ask the students in your class that would result in numerical data. For each question, explain how you know that responses to it would produce numerical data.

4. Triangle DEF has vertices $D = (-4, -4)$, $E = (-2, -4)$, and $F = (-3, -1)$.

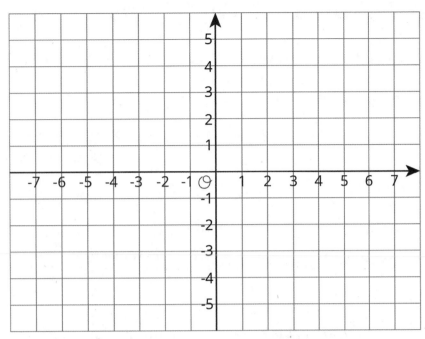

a. Plot the triangle in the coordinate plane and label the vertices.

b. Name the coordinates of 3 points that are inside the triangle.

c. What is the area of the triangle? Show your reasoning.

(From Unit 7, Lesson 15.)

Lesson 2: Statistical Questions

Let's look more closely at data and the questions they can help to answer.

2.1: Pencils on A Plot

1. Measure your pencil to the nearest $\frac{1}{4}$-inch. Then, plot your measurement on the class dot plot.

2. What is the difference between the longest and shortest pencil lengths in the class?

3. What is the most common pencil length?

4. Find the difference in lengths between the most common length and the shortest pencil.

2.2: What's in the Data?

Ten sixth-grade students at a school were each asked five survey questions. Their answers to each question are shown here.

data set A	0	1	1	3	0	0	0	2	1	1
data set B	12	12	12	12	12	12	12	12	12	12
data set C	6	5	7	6	4	5	3	4	6	8
data set D	6	6	6	6	6	6	6	6	6	6
data set E	3	7	9	11	6	4	2	16	6	10

1. Here are the five survey questions. Match each question to a data set that could represent the students' answers. Explain your reasoning.

   - Question 1: Flip a coin 10 times. How many heads did you get?

   - Question 2: How many books did you read in the last year?

   - Question 3: What grade are you in?

   - Question 4: How many dogs and cats do you have?

   - Question 5: How many inches are in 1 foot?

2. How are survey questions 3 and 5 different from the other questions?

2.3: What Makes a Statistical Question?

These three questions are examples of **statistical questions**:

- What is the most common color of the cars in the school parking lot?

- What percentage of students in the school have a cell phone?

- Which kind of literature—fiction or nonfiction—is more popular among students in the school?

These three questions are not examples of **statistical questions**:

- What color is the principal's car?

- Does Elena have a cell phone?

- What kind of literature—fiction or nonfiction—does Diego prefer?

1. Study the examples and non-examples. Discuss with your partner:

   a. How are the three statistical questions alike? What do they have in common?

   b. How are the three non-statistical questions alike? What do they have in common?

   c. How can you find answers to the statistical questions? How about answers to non-statistical questions?

   d. What makes a question a statistical question?

   Pause here for a class discussion.

iM KH

2. Read each question. Think about the data you might collect to answer it and whether you expect to see **variability** in the data. Complete each blank with "Yes" or "No."

a. How many cups of water do my classmates drink each day?

- Is variability expected in the data? _____

- Is the question statistical? _____

b. Where in town does our math teacher live?

- Is variability expected in the data? _____

- Is the question statistical? _____

c. How many minutes does it take students in my class to get ready for school in the morning?

- Is variability expected in the data? _____

- Is the question statistical? _____

d. How many minutes of recess do sixth-grade students have each day?

- Is variability expected in the data? _____

- Is the question statistical? _____

e. Do all students in my class know what month it is?

- Is variability expected in the data? _____

- Is the question statistical? _____

2.4: Sifting for Statistical Questions

1. Your teacher will give you and your partner a set of cards with questions. Sort them into three piles: Statistical Questions, Not Statistical Questions, and Unsure.

2. Compare your sorting decisions with another group of students. Start by discussing the two piles that your group sorted into the Statistical Questions and Not Statistical Questions piles. Then, review the cards in the Unsure pile. Discuss the questions until both groups reach an agreement and have no cards left in the Unsure pile. If you get stuck, think about whether the question could be answered by collecting data and if there would be variability in that data.

3. Record the letter names of the questions in each pile.

   ○ Statistical questions: ○ Non-statistical questions:

Are you ready for more?

Tyler and Han are discussing the question, "Which sixth-grade student lives the farthest from school?"

- Tyler says, "I don't think the question is a statistical question. There is only one person who lives the farthest from school, so there would not be variability in the data we collect."

- Han says: "I think it is a statistical question. To answer the question, we wouldn't actually be asking everyone, 'Which student lives the farthest from school?' We would have to ask each student how far away from school they live, and we can expect their responses to have variability."

Do you agree with either one of them? Explain your reasoning.

Lesson 2 Summary

We often collect data to answer questions about something. The data we collect may show **variability**, which means the data values are not all the same.

Some data sets have more variability than others. Here are two sets of figures.

 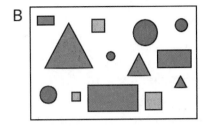

Set A has more figures with the same shape, color, or size. Set B shows more figures with different shapes, colors, or sizes, so set B has greater variability than set A.

Both numerical and categorical data can show variability. Numerical sets can contain different numbers, and categorical sets can contain different categories or types.

When a question can only be answered by using data and we expect that data to have variability, we call it a **statistical question**. Here are some examples.

- Who is the most popular musical artist at your school?
- When do students in your class typically eat dinner?
- Which classroom in your school has the most books?

To answer the question about books, we may need to count all of the books in each classroom of a school. The data we collect would likely show variability because we would expect each classroom to have a different number of books.

In contrast, the question "How many books are in your classroom?" is *not* a statistical question. If we collect data to answer the question (for example, by asking everyone in the class to count books), the data can be expected to show the same value. Likewise, if we ask all of the students at a school where they go to school, that question is not a statistical question because the responses will all be the same.

Glossary

- statistical question
- variability

Lesson 2 Practice Problems

1. Sixth-grade students were asked, "What grade are you in?" Explain why this is *not a* statistical question.

2. Lin and her friends went out for ice cream after school. The following questions came up during their trip. Select **all** the questions that are statistical questions.

   A. How far are we from the ice cream shop?

   B. What is the most popular ice cream flavor this week?

   C. What does a group of 4 people typically spend on ice cream at this shop?

   D. Do kids usually prefer to get a cup or a cone?

   E. How many toppings are there to choose from?

3. Here is a list of questions about the students and teachers at a school. Select **all** the questions that are statistical questions.

   A. What is the most popular lunch choice?

   B. What school do these students attend?

   C. How many math teachers are in the school?

   D. What is a common age for the teachers at the school?

   E. About how many hours of sleep do students generally get on a school night?

   F. How do students usually travel from home to school?

iM KH

4. Here is a list of statistical questions. What data would you collect and analyze to answer each question? For numerical data, include the unit of measurement that you would use.

   a. What is a typical height of female athletes on a team in the most recent international sporting event?

   b. Are most adults in the school football fans?

   c. How long do drivers generally need to wait at a red light in Washington, DC?

5. Describe the scale you would use on the coordinate plane to plot each set of points. What value would you assign to each unit of the grid?

   a. $(1, -6), (-7, -8), (-3, 7), (0, 9)$

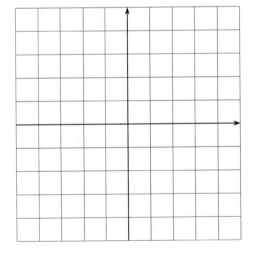

   b. $(-20, -30), (-40, 10), (20, -10), (5, -20)$

   c. $(\frac{-1}{3}, -1), (\frac{2}{3}, -1\frac{1}{3}), (\frac{-4}{3}, \frac{2}{3}), (\frac{1}{6}, 0)$

(From Unit 7, Lesson 13.)

6. Noah's water bottle contains more than 1 quart of water but less than $1\frac{1}{2}$ quarts. Let w be the amount of water in Noah's bottle, in quarts. Select **all** the true statements.

A. w could be $\frac{3}{4}$.

B. w could be 1.

C. $w > 1$

D. w could be $\frac{4}{3}$.

E. w could be $\frac{5}{4}$.

F. w could be $\frac{5}{3}$.

G. $w > 1.5$

(From Unit 7, Lesson 9.)

7. Order these numbers from least to greatest:

|-17| |-18| -18 |19| 20

(From Unit 7, Lesson 7.)

iM KH

Lesson 3: Representing Data Graphically

Let's represent data with dot plots and bar graphs.

3.1: Curious about Caps

Clare collects bottle caps and keeps them in plastic containers.

Write one statistical question that someone could ask Clare about her collection. Be prepared to explain your reasoning.

3.2: Estimating Caps

1. Write down the statistical question your class is trying to answer.

2. Look at the dot plot that shows the data from your class. Write down one thing you notice and one thing you wonder about the dot plot.

3. Use the dot plot to answer the statistical question. Be prepared to explain your reasoning.

3.3: Been There, Done That!

Priya wants to know if basketball players on a men's team and a women's team have had prior experience in international competitions. She gathered data on the number of times the players were on a team before 2016.

men's team

3   0   0   0   0   1   0   0   0   0   0   0

women's team

2   3   3   1   0   2   0   1   1   0   3   1

1. Did Priya collect categorical or numerical data?

2. Organize the information on the two basketball teams into these tables.

Men's Basketball Team Players

number of prior competitions	frequency (number)
0	
1	
2	
3	
4	

Women's Basketball Team Players

number of prior competitions	frequency (number)
0	
1	
2	
3	
4	

iM KH

3. Make a dot plot for each table.

Men's Basketball Team Players   Women's Basketball Team Players

number of prior competitions   number of prior competitions

4. Study your dot plots. What do they tell you about the competition participation of:

   a. the players on the men's basketball team?

   b. the players on the women's basketball team?

5. Explain why a dot plot is an appropriate representation for Priya's data.

Are you ready for more?

Combine the data for the players on the men's and women's teams and represent it as a single dot plot. What can you say about the repeat participation of the basketball players?

number of prior competitions

3.4: Favorite Summer Sports

Kiran wants to know which three summer sports are most popular in his class. He surveyed his classmates on their favorite summer sport. Here are their responses.

swimming	gymnastics	track and field	volleyball
swimming	swimming	diving	track and field
gymnastics	basketball	basketball	volleyball
track and field	track and field	volleyball	gymnastics
diving	gymnastics	volleyball	rowing
track and field	track and field	soccer	swimming
gymnastics	track and field	swimming	rowing
diving	soccer		

1. Did Kiran collect categorical or numerical data?

2. Organize the responses in a table to help him find which summer sports are most popular in his class.

sport	frequency

iM KH

3. Represent the information in the table as a bar graph.

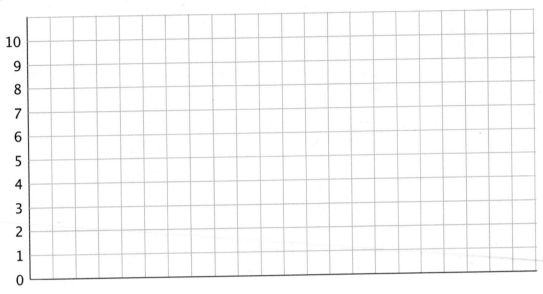

4.   a. How can you use the bar graph to find how many classmates Kiran surveyed?

      b. Which three summer sports are most popular in Kiran's class?

      c. Use your bar graph to describe at least one observation about Kiran's classmates' preferred summer sports.

5. Could a dot plot be used to represent Kiran's data? Explain your reasoning.

Lesson 3 Summary

When we analyze data, we are often interested in the **distribution**, which is information that shows all the data values and how often they occur.

In a previous lesson, we saw data about 10 dogs. We can see the distribution of the dog weights in a table such as this one.

weight in kilograms	frequency
6	1
7	3
10	2
32	1
35	2
36	1

The term **frequency** refers to the number of times a data value occurs. In this case, we see that there are three dogs that weigh 7 kilograms, so "3" is the frequency for the value "7 kilograms."

Recall that dot plots are often used to to represent numerical data. Like a frequency table, a dot plot also shows the distribution of a data set. This dot plot, which you saw in an earlier lesson, shows the distribution of dog weights.

dog weights in kilograms

A dot plot uses a horizontal number line. We show the frequency of a value by the number of dots drawn above that value. Here, the two dots above the number 35 tell us that there are two dogs weighing 35 kilograms.

iM KH

The distribution of categorical data can also be shown in a table. This table shows the distribution of dog breeds.

breed	frequency
pug	9
beagle	9
German shepherd	12

We often represent the distribution of categorical data using a bar graph.

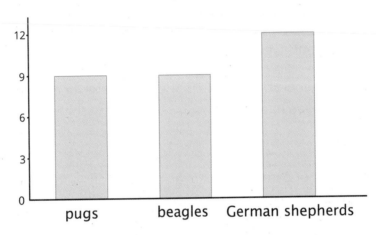

A bar graph also uses a horizontal line. Above it we draw a rectangle (or "bar") to represent each category in the data set. The height of a bar tells us the frequency of the category. There are 12 German shepherds in the data set, so the bar for this category is 12 units tall. Below the line we write the labels for the categories.

In a dot plot, a data value is placed according to its position on the number line. A weight of 10 kilograms must be shown as a dot above 10 on the number line.

In a bar graph, however, the categories can be listed in any order. The bar that shows the frequency of pugs can be placed anywhere along the horizontal line.

Glossary

- distribution
- frequency

Lesson 3 Practice Problems

1. A teacher drew a line segment that was 20 inches long on the blackboard. She asked each of her students to estimate the length of the segment and used their estimates to draw this dot plot.

estimated length in inches

   a. How many students were in the class?

   b. Were students generally accurate in their estimates of the length of the line? Explain your reasoning.

2. Here are descriptions of data sets. Select **all** descriptions of data sets that could be graphed as dot plots.

   A. Class size for the classes at an elementary school

   B. Colors of cars in a parking lot

   C. Favorite sport of each student in a sixth-grade class

   D. Birth weights for the babies born during October at a hospital

   E. Number of goals scored in each of 20 games played by a school soccer team

3. Priya recorded the number of attempts it took each of 12 of her classmates to successfully throw a ball into a basket. Make a dot plot of Priya's data.

   1   2   1   3   1   4   4   3   1   2   5   2

iM KH

4. Solve each equation.

   a. $9v = 1$

   b. $1.37w = 0$

   c. $1 = \frac{7}{10}x$

   d. $12.1 = 12.1 + y$

   e. $\frac{3}{5} + z = 1$

   (From Unit 6, Lesson 4.)

5. Find the quotients.

   a. $\frac{2}{5} \div 2$

   b. $\frac{2}{5} \div 5$

   c. $2 \div \frac{2}{5}$

   d. $5 \div \frac{2}{5}$

   (From Unit 4, Lesson 11.)

6. Find the area of each triangle.

A B   C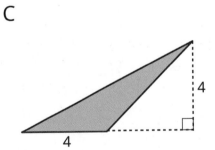

   (From Unit 1, Lesson 9.)

Lesson 4: Dot Plots

Let's investigate what dot plots and bar graphs can tell us.

4.1: Pizza Toppings (Part 1)

Fifteen customers in a pizza shop were asked, "How many toppings did you add to your cheese pizza?" Here are their responses:

1	2	1	3	0	1	1	2
0	3	0	0	1	2	2	

1. Could you use a dot plot to represent the data? Explain your reasoning.

2. Complete the table.

number of toppings	frequency (number)
0	
1	
2	
3	

4.2: Pizza Toppings (Part 2)

1. Use the tables from the warm-up to display the number of toppings as a dot plot. Label your drawing clearly.

2. Use your dot plot to study the distribution for number of toppings. What do you notice about the number of toppings that this group of customers ordered? Write 2–3 sentences summarizing your observations.

Are you ready for more?

Think of a statistical question that can be answered with the data about the number of toppings ordered, as displayed on the dot plot. Then answer this question.

4.3: Homework Time

Twenty-five sixth-grade students answered the question: "How many hours do you generally spend on homework each week?"

This dot plot shows the number of hours per week that these 25 students reported spending on homework.

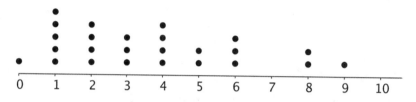

hours spent on homework per week

Use the dot plot to answer the following questions. For each, show or explain your reasoning.

1. What percentage of the students reported spending 1 hour on homework each week?

2. What percentage of the students reported spending 4 or fewer hours on homework each week?

3. Would 6 hours per week be a good description of the number of hours this group of students spends on homework per week? What about 1 hour per week? Explain your reasoning.

4. What value do you think would be a good description of the homework time of the students in this group? Explain your reasoning.

5. Someone said, "In general, these students spend roughly the same number of hours doing homework." Do you agree? Explain your reasoning.

iM KH

Lesson 4 Summary

We often collect and analyze data because we are interested in learning what is "typical," or what is common and can be expected in a group.

Sometimes it is easy to tell what a typical member of the group is. For example, we can say that a typical shape in this set is a large circle.

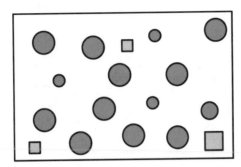

Just looking at the members of a group doesn't always tell us what is typical, however. For example, if we are interested in the side length typical of squares in this set, it isn't easy to do so just by studying the set visually.

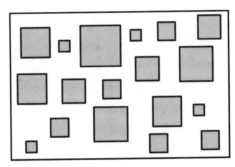

In a situation like this, it is helpful to gather the side lengths of the squares in the set and look at their distribution, as shown in this dot plot.

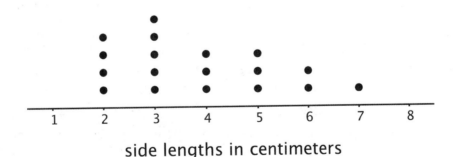

side lengths in centimeters

We can see that many of the data points are between 2 and 4, so we could say that side lengths between 2 and 4 centimeters or close to these lengths are typical of squares in this set.

Lesson 4 Practice Problems

1. Clare recorded the amounts of time spent doing homework, in hours per week, by students in sixth, eighth, and tenth grades. She made a dot plot of the data for each grade and provided the following summary.

   ○ Students in sixth grade tend to spend less time on homework than students in eighth and tenth grades.

   ○ The homework times for the tenth-grade students are more alike than the homework times for the eighth-grade students.

   Use Clare's summary to match each dot plot to the correct grade (sixth, eighth, or tenth).

   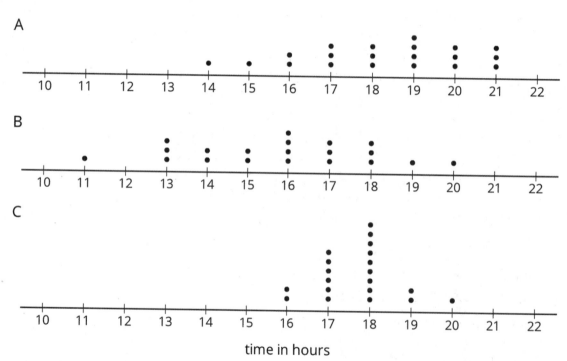

2. Mai played 10 basketball games. She recorded the number of points she scored and made a dot plot. Mai said that she scored between 8 and 14 points in most of the 10 games, but one game was exceptional. During that game she scored more than double her typical score of 9 points. Use the number line to make a dot plot that fits the description Mai gave.

iM KH

3. A movie theater is showing three different movies. The dot plots represent the ages of the people who were at the Saturday afternoon showing of each of these movies.

age

a. One of these movies was an animated movie rated G for general audiences. Do you think it was movie A, B, or C? Explain your reasoning.

b. Which movie has a dot plot with ages that that center at about 30 years?

c. What is a typical age for the people who were at Movie A?

4. Find the value of each expression.

a. $3.727 + 1.384$

b. $3.727 - 1.384$

c. $5.01 \cdot 4.8$

d. $5.01 \div 4.8$

(From Unit 5, Lesson 13.)

Lesson 5: Using Dot Plots to Answer Statistical Questions

Let's use dot plots to describe distributions and answer questions.

5.1: Packs on Backs

This dot plot shows the weights of backpacks, in kilograms, of 50 sixth-grade students at a school in New Zealand.

weight in kilograms

1. The dot plot shows several dots at 0 kilograms. What could a value of 0 mean in this context?

2. Clare and Tyler studied the dot plot.

   ○ Clare said, "I think we can use 3 kilograms to describe a typical backpack weight of the group because it represents 20%—or the largest portion—of the data."

   ○ Tyler disagreed and said, "I think 3 kilograms is too low to describe a typical weight. Half of the dots are for backpacks that are heavier than 3 kilograms, so I would use a larger value."

   Do you agree with either of them? Explain your reasoning.

iM KH

5.2: On the Phone

Twenty-five sixth-grade students were asked to estimate how many hours a week they spend talking on the phone. This dot plot represents their reported number of hours of phone usage per week.

hours on the phone per week

1. a. How many of the students reported not talking on the phone during the week? Explain how you know.

    b. What percentage of the students reported not talking on the phone?

2. a. What is the largest number of hours a student spent talking on the phone per week?

    b. What percentage of the group reported talking on the phone for this amount of time?

3. a. How many hours would you say that these students typically spend talking on the phone?

    b. How many minutes per day would that be?

4. a. How would you describe the **spread** of the data? Would you consider these students' amounts of time on the phone to be alike or different? Explain your reasoning.

    b. Here is the dot plot from an earlier activity. It shows the number of hours per week the same group of 25 sixth-grade students reported spending on homework.

    hours spent on homework per week

    Overall, are these students more alike in the amount of time they spend talking on the phone or in the amount of time they spend on homework? Explain your reasoning.

5. Suppose someone claimed that these sixth-grade students spend too much time on the phone. Do you agree? Use your analysis of the dot plot to support your answer.

iᴍ KH

5.3: Click-Clack

1. A keyboarding teacher wondered: "Do typing speeds of students improve after taking a keyboarding course?" Explain why her question is a statistical question.

2. The teacher recorded the number of words that her students could type per minute at the beginning of a course and again at the end. The two dot plots show the two data sets.

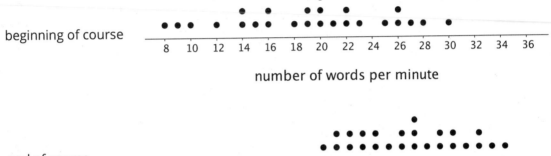

Based on the dot plots, do you agree with each of the following statements about this group of students? Be prepared to explain your reasoning.

a. Overall, the students' typing speed did not improve. They typed at the same speed at the end of the course as they did at the beginning.

b. 20 words per minute is a good estimate for how fast, in general, the students typed at the beginning of the course.

c. 20 words per minute is a good description of the **center** of the data set at the end of the course.

d. There was more variability in the typing speeds at the beginning of the course than at the end, so the students' typing speeds were more alike at the end.

3. Overall, how fast would you say that the students typed after completing the course? What would you consider the center of the end-of-course data?

Are you ready for more?

Use one of these suggestions (or make up your own). Research to create a dot plot with at least 10 values. Then, describe the center and spread of the distribution.

- Points scored by your favorite sports team in its last 10 games
- Length of your 10 favorite movies (in minutes)
- Ages of your favorite 10 celebrities

iM KH

Lesson 5 Summary

One way to describe what is typical or characteristic for a data set is by looking at the **center** and **spread** of its distribution.

Let's compare the distribution of cat weights and dog weights shown on these dot plots.

cat weights in kilograms

dog weights in kilograms

The collection of points for the cat data is further to the left on the number line than the dog data. Based on the dot plots, we may describe the center of the distribution for cat weights to be between 4 and 5 kilograms and the center for dog weights to be between 7 and 8 kilograms.

We often say that values at or near the center of a distribution are typical for that group. This means that a weight of 4–5 kilograms is typical for a cat in the data set, and weight of 7–8 kilograms is typical for a dog.

We also see that the dog weights are more spread out than the cat weights. The difference between the heaviest and lightest cats is only 4 kilograms, but the difference between the heaviest and lightest dogs is 6 kilograms.

A distribution with greater spread tells us that the data have greater variability. In this case, we could say that the cats are more similar in their weights than the dogs.

In future lessons, we will discuss how to measure the center and spread of a distribution.

Glossary

- center
- spread

Lesson 5 Practice Problems

1. Three sets of data about ten sixth-grade students were used to make three dot plots. The person who made these dot plots forgot to label them. Match each dot plot with the appropriate label.

A

B

C
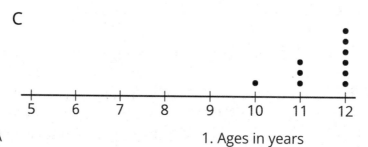

A. Dot Plot A

B. Dot Plot B

C. Dot Plot C

1. Ages in years

2. Numbers of hours of sleep on nights before school days

3. Numbers of hours of sleep on nights before non-school days

2. The dot plots show the time it takes to get to school for ten sixth-grade students from the United States, Canada, Australia, New Zealand, and South Africa.

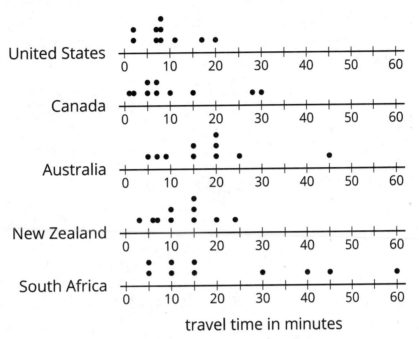

travel time in minutes

a. List the countries in order of *typical travel times*, from shortest to longest.

b. List the countries in order of *variability in travel times*, from the least variability to the greatest.

3. Twenty-five students were asked to rate—on a scale of 0 to 10—how important it is to reduce pollution. A rating of 0 means "not at all important" and a rating of 10 means "very important." Here is a dot plot of their responses.

importance of reducing pollution

Explain why a rating of 6 is *not* a good description of the center of this data set.

4. Tyler wants to buy some cherries at the farmer's market. He has $10 and cherries cost $4 per pound.

   a. If c is the number of pounds of cherries that Tyler can buy, write one or more inequalities or equations describing c.

   b. Can 2 be a value of c? Can 3 be a value of c? What about -1? Explain your reasoning.

   c. If m is the amount of money, in dollars, Tyler can spend, write one or more inequalities or equations describing m.

   d. Can 8 be a value of m? Can 2 be a value of m? What about 10.5? Explain your reasoning.

(From Unit 7, Lesson 10.)

Lesson 6: Interpreting Histograms

Let's explore how histograms represent data sets.

6.1: Dog Show (Part 1)

Here is a dot plot showing the weights, in pounds, of 40 dogs at a dog show.

weight in pounds

1. Write two statistical questions that can be answered using the dot plot.

2. What would you consider a typical weight for a dog at this dog show? Explain your reasoning.

6.2: Dog Show (Part 2)

Here is a **histogram** that shows some dog weights in pounds.

weight in pounds

Each bar includes the left-end value but not the right-end value. For example, the first bar includes dogs that weigh 60 pounds and 68 pounds but not 80 pounds.

1. Use the histogram to answer the following questions.

   a. How many dogs weigh at least 100 pounds?

   b. How many dogs weigh exactly 70 pounds?

   c. How many dogs weigh at least 120 and less than 160 pounds?

   d. How much does the heaviest dog at the show weigh?

   e. What would you consider a typical weight for a dog at this dog show? Explain your reasoning.

2. Discuss with a partner:

   ○ If you used the dot plot to answer the same five questions you just answered, how would your answers be different?

   ○ How are the histogram and the dot plot alike? How are they different?

iM KH

6.3: Population of States

Every ten years, the United States conducts a census, which is an effort to count the entire population. The dot plot shows the population data from the 2010 census for each of the fifty states and the District of Columbia (DC).

population of states in millions

1. Here are some statistical questions about the population of the fifty states and DC. How difficult would it be to answer the questions using the *dot plot*?

   In the middle column, rate each question with an E (easy to answer), H (hard to answer), or I (impossible to answer). Be prepared to explain your reasoning.

statistical question	using the dot plot	using the histogram
a. How many states have populations greater than 15 million?		
b. Which states have populations greater than 15 million?		
c. How many states have populations less than 5 million?		
d. What is a typical state population?		
e. Are there more states with fewer than 5 million people or more states with between 5 and 10 million people?		
f. How would you describe the distribution of state populations?		

2. Here are the population data for all states and the District of Columbia from the 2010 census. Use the information to complete the table.

Alabama	4.78	Illinois	12.83	Montana	0.99	Rhode Island	1.05
Alaska	0.71	Indiana	6.48	Nebraska	1.83	South Carolina	4.63
Arizona	6.39	Iowa	3.05	Nevada	2.70	South Dakota	0.81
Arkansas	2.92	Kansas	2.85	New Hampshire	1.32	Tennessee	6.35
California	37.25	Kentucky	4.34	New Jersey	8.79	Texas	25.15
Colorado	5.03	Louisiana	4.53	New Mexico	2.06	Utah	2.76
Connecticut	3.57	Maine	1.33	New York	19.38	Vermont	0.63
Delaware	0.90	Maryland	5.77	North Carolina	9.54	Virginia	8.00
District of Columbia	0.60	Massachusetts	6.55	North Dakota	0.67	Washington	6.72
Florida	18.80	Michigan	9.88	Ohio	11.54	West Virginia	1.85
Georgia	9.69	Minnesota	5.30	Oklahoma	3.75	Wisconsin	5.69
Hawaii	1.36	Mississippi	2.97	Oregon	3.83	Wyoming	0.56
Idaho	1.57	Missouri	5.99	Pennsylvania	12.70		

population (millions)	frequency
0–5	
5–10	
10–15	
15–20	
20–25	
25–30	
30–35	
35–40	

3. Use the grid and the information in your table to create a histogram.

population of states in millions

4. Return to the statistical questions at the beginning of the activity. Which ones are now easier to answer?

In the last column of the table, rate each question with an E (easy), H (hard), and I (impossible) based on how difficult it is to answer them. Be prepared to explain your reasoning.

Are you ready for more?

Think of two more statistical questions that can be answered using the data about populations of states. Then, decide whether each question can be answered using the dot plot, the histogram, or both.

Lesson 6 Summary

In addition to using dot plots, we can also represent distributions of numerical data using **histograms**.

Here is a dot plot that shows the weights, in kilograms, of 30 dogs, followed by a histogram that shows the same distribution.

dog weights in kilograms

dog weights in kilograms

In a histogram, data values are placed in groups or "bins" of a certain size, and each group is represented with a bar. The height of the bar tells us the frequency for that group.

For example, the height of the tallest bar is 10, and the bar represents weights from 20 to less than 25 kilograms, so there are 10 dogs whose weights fall in that group. Similarly, there are 3 dogs that weigh anywhere from 25 to less than 30 kilograms.

Notice that the histogram and the dot plot have a similar shape. The dot plot has the advantage of showing all of the data values, but the histogram is easier to draw and to interpret when there are a lot of values or when the values are all different.

iM KH

Here is a dot plot showing the weight distribution of 40 dogs. The weights were measured to the nearest 0.1 kilogram instead of the nearest kilogram.

dog weights in kilograms

Here is a histogram showing the same distribution.

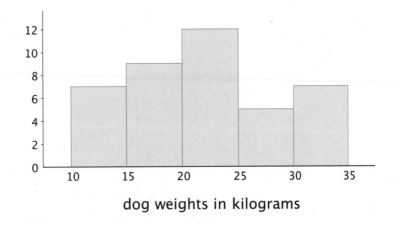

dog weights in kilograms

In this case, it is difficult to make sense of the distribution from the dot plot because the dots are so close together and all in one line. The histogram of the same data set does a much better job showing the distribution of weights, even though we can't see the individual data values.

Glossary

- histogram

Lesson 6 Practice Problems

1. Match histograms A through E to dot plots 1 through 5 so that each match represents the same data set.

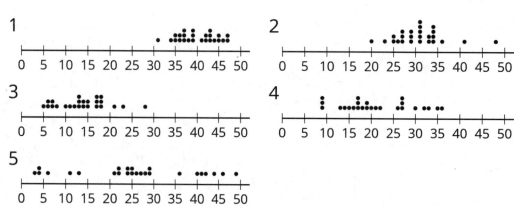

iM KH

2. (-2, 3) is one vertex of a square on a coordinate plane. Name three points that could be the other vertices.

(From Unit 7, Lesson 12.)

3. Here is a histogram that summarizes the lengths, in feet, of a group of adult female sharks. Select **all** the statements that are true, according to the histogram.

length in feet

A. A total of 9 sharks were measured.

B. A total of 50 sharks were measured.

C. The longest shark that was measured was 10 feet long.

D. Most of the sharks that were measured were over 16 feet long.

E. Two of the sharks that were measured were less than 14 feet long.

4. This table shows the times, in minutes, it took 40 sixth-grade students to run 1 mile.

time (minutes)	frequency
4 to less than 6	1
6 to less than 8	5
8 to less than 10	13
10 to less than 12	12
12 to less than 14	7
14 to less than 16	2

Draw a histogram for the information in the table.

iM KH

Lesson 7: Using Histograms to Answer Statistical Questions

Let's draw histograms and use them to answer questions.

7.1: Which One Doesn't Belong: Questions

Here are four questions about the population of Alaska. Which question does not belong? Be prepared to explain your reasoning.

1. In general, at what age do Alaska residents retire?

2. At what age can Alaskans vote?

3. What is the age difference between the youngest and oldest Alaska residents with a full-time job?

4. Which age group is the largest part of the population: 18 years or younger, 19–25 years, 25–34 years, 35–44 years, 45–54 years, 55–64 years, or 65 years or older?

7.2: Measuring Earthworms

An earthworm farmer set up several containers of a certain species of earthworms so that he could learn about their lengths. The lengths of the earthworms provide information about their ages. The farmer measured the lengths of 25 earthworms in one of the containers. Each length was measured in millimeters.

1. Using a ruler, draw a line segment for each length:

   ○ 20 millimeters

   ○ 40 millimeters

   ○ 60 millimeters

   ○ 80 millimeters

   ○ 100 millimeters

2. Here are the lengths, in millimeters, of the 25 earthworms.

6	11	18	19	20	23	23	25
25	26	27	27	28	29	32	33
41	42	48	52	54	59	60	77
93							

Complete the table for the lengths of the 25 earthworms.

length	frequency
0 millimeters to less than 20 millimeters	
20 millimeters to less than 40 millimeters	
40 millimeters to less than 60 millimeters	
60 millimeters to less than 80 millimeters	
80 millimeters to less than 100 millimeters	

3. Use the grid and the information in the table to draw a histogram for the worm length data. Be sure to label the axes of your histogram.

4. Based on the histogram, what is a typical length for these 25 earthworms? Explain how you know.

5. Write 1–2 sentences to describe the spread of the data. Do most of the worms have a length that is close to your estimate of a typical length, or are they very different in length?

Are you ready for more?

Here is another histogram for the earthworm measurement data. In this histogram, the measurements are in different groupings.

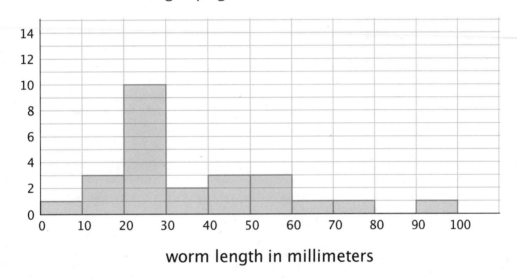

worm length in millimeters

1. Based on this histogram, what is your estimate of a typical length for the 25 earthworms?

2. Compare this histogram with the one you drew. How are the distributions of data summarized in the two histograms the same? How are they different?

3. Compare your estimates of a typical earthworm length for the two histograms. Did you reach different conclusions about a typical earthworm length from the two histograms?

7.3: Tall and Taller Players

Professional basketball players tend to be taller than professional baseball players.

Here are two histograms that show height distributions of 50 male professional baseball players and 50 male professional basketball players.

1. Decide which histogram shows the heights of baseball players and which shows the heights of basketball players. Be prepared to explain your reasoning.

height in inches

2. Write 2–3 sentences that describe the distribution of the heights of the basketball players. Comment on the center and spread of the data.

3. Write 2–3 sentences that describe the distribution of the heights of the baseball players. Comment on the center and spread of the data.

iM KH

Lesson 7 Summary

Here are the weights, in kilograms, of 30 dogs.

10	11	12	12	13	15	16	16
17	18	18	19	20	20	20	21
22	22	22	23	24	24	26	26
28	30	32	32	34	34		

Before we draw a histogram, let's consider a couple of questions.

- What are the smallest and largest values in our data set? This gives us an idea of the distance on the number line that our histogram will cover. In this case, the minimum is 10 and the maximum is 34, so our number line needs to extend from 10 to 35 at the very least.

  (Remember the convention we use to mark off the number line for a histogram: we include the left boundary of a bar but exclude the right boundary. If 34 is the right boundary of the last bar, it won't be included in that bar, so the number line needs to go a little greater than the maximum value.)

- What group size or bin size seems reasonable here? We could organize the weights into bins of 2 kilograms (10, 12, 14, . . .), 5 kilograms, (10, 15, 20, 25, . . .), 10 kilograms (10, 20, 30, . . .), or any other size. The smaller the bins, the more bars we will have, and vice versa.

Let's use bins of 5 kilograms for the dog weights. The boundaries of our bins will be: 10, 15, 20, 25, 30, 35. We stop at 35 because it is greater than the maximum.

Next, we find the frequency for the values in each group. It is helpful to organize the values in a table.

weights in kilograms	frequency
10 to less than 15	5
15 to less than 20	7
20 to less than 25	10
25 to less than 30	3
30 to less than 35	5

Now we can draw the histogram.

dog weights in kilograms

The histogram allows us to learn more about the dog weight distribution and describe its center and spread.

Lesson 7 Practice Problems

1. These two histograms show the number of text messages sent in one week by two groups of 100 students. The first histogram summarizes data from sixth-grade students. The second histogram summarizes data from seventh-grade students.

text messages sent per week by sixth-grade students

text messages sent per week by seventh-grade students

a. Do the two data sets have approximately the same center? If so, explain where the center is located. If not, which one has the greater center?

b. Which data set has greater spread? Explain your reasoning.

c. Overall, which group of students—sixth- or seventh-grade—sent more text messages?

2. Forty sixth-grade students ran 1 mile. Here is a histogram that summarizes their times, in minutes. The center of the distribution is approximately 10 minutes.

On the blank axes, draw a second histogram that has:

- a distribution of times for a different group of 40 sixth-grade students.
- a center at 10 minutes.
- less variability than the distribution shown in the first histogram.

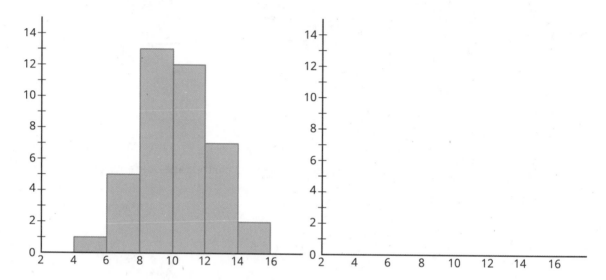

3. Jada has d dimes. She has more than 30 cents but less than a dollar.

   a. Write two inequalities that represent how many dimes Jada has.

   b. Can d be 10?

   c. How many possible solutions make both inequalities true? If possible, describe or list the solutions.

(From Unit 7, Lesson 9.)

4. Order these numbers from greatest to least: -4, $\frac{1}{4}$, 0, 4, $-3\frac{1}{2}$, $\frac{7}{4}$, $-\frac{5}{4}$

(From Unit 7, Lesson 4.)

iM KH

Lesson 8: Describing Distributions on Histograms

Let's describe distributions displayed in histograms.

8.1: Which One Doesn't Belong: Histograms

Which histogram does not belong? Be prepared to explain your reasoning.

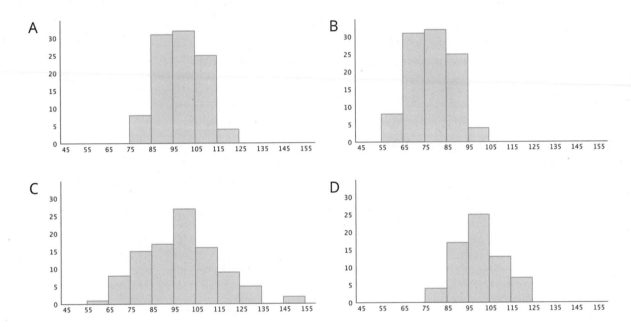

8.2: Sorting Histograms

1. Your teacher will give your group a set of histogram cards. Sort them into two piles—one for histograms that are approximately symmetrical, and another for those that are not.

2. Discuss your sorting decisions with another group. Do both groups agree which cards should go in each pile? If not, discuss the reasons behind the differences and see if you can reach agreement. Record your final decisions.

   ○ Histograms that are approximately symmetrical:

   ○ Histograms that are not approximately symmetrical:

3. Histograms are also described by how many major peaks they have. Histogram A is an example of a distribution with a single peak that is not symmetrical.

   Which other histograms have this feature?

4. Some histograms have a gap, a space between two bars where there are no data points. For example, if some students in a class have 7 or more siblings, but the rest of the students have 0, 1, or 2 siblings, the histogram for this data set would show gaps between the bars because no students have 3, 4, 5, or 6 siblings.

   Which histograms do you think show one or more gaps?

5. Sometimes there are a few data points in a data set that are far from the center. Histogram A is an example of a distribution with this feature.

   Which other histograms have this feature?

8.3: Getting to School

Your teacher will provide you with some data that your class collected the other day.

1. Use the data to draw a histogram that shows your class's travel times.

travel time in minutes

2. Describe the distribution of travel times. Comment on the center and spread of the data, as well as the shape and features.

3. Use the data on methods of travel to draw a bar graph. Include labels for the horizontal axis.

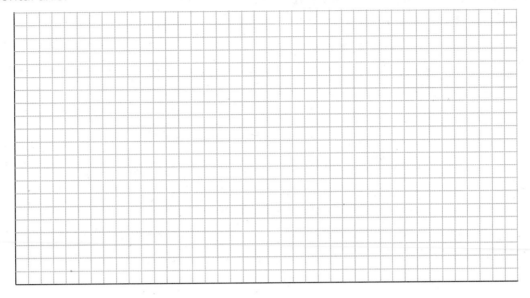

4. Describe what you learned about your class's methods of transportation to school. Comment on any patterns you noticed.

5. Compare the histogram and the bar graph that you drew. How are they the same? How are they different?

Are you ready for more?

Use one of these suggestions (or make up your own). Research data to create a histogram. Then, describe the distribution.

- Heights of 30 athletes from multiple sports
- Heights of 30 athletes from the same sport
- High temperatures for each day of the last month in a city you would like to visit
- Prices for all the menu items at a local restaurant

Lesson 8 Summary

We can describe the shape and features of the distribution shown on a histogram. Here are two distributions with very different shapes and features.

- Histogram A is very symmetrical and has a peak near 21. Histogram B is not symmetrical and has two peaks, one near 11 and one near 25.

- Histogram B has two clusters. A cluster forms when many data points are near a particular value (or a neighborhood of values) on a number line.

- Histogram B also has a gap between 20 and 22. A gap shows a location with no data values.

Here is a bar graph showing the breeds of 30 dogs and a histogram for their weights.

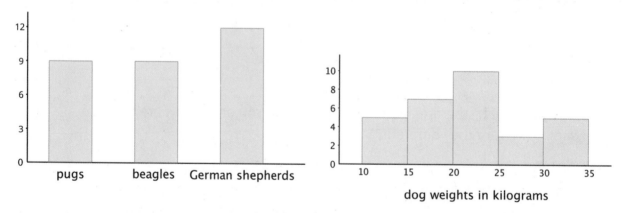

Bar graphs and histograms may seem alike, but they are very different.

- Bar graphs represent categorical data. Histograms represent numerical data.

- Bar graphs have spaces between the bars. Histograms show a space between bars *only* when no data values fall between the bars.

- Bars in a bar graph can be in any order. Histograms must be in numerical order.

- In a bar graph, the number of bars depends on the number of categories. In a histogram, we choose how many bars to use.

iM KH

Lesson 8 Practice Problems

1. The histogram summarizes the data on the body lengths of 143 wild bears. Describe the distribution of body lengths. Be sure to comment on shape, center, and spread.

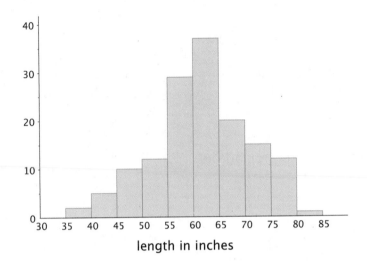

2. Which data set is more likely to produce a histogram with a symmetric distribution? Explain your reasoning.

   ○ Data on the number of seconds on a track of music in a pop album.
   ○ Data on the number of seconds spent talking on the phone yesterday by everyone in the school.

3. Evaluate the expression $4x^3$ for each value of x.

   a. 1

   b. 2

   c. $\frac{1}{2}$

   (From Unit 6, Lesson 15.)

4. Decide if each data set might produce one or more gaps when represented by a histogram. For each data set that you think might produce gaps, briefly describe or give an example of how the values in the data set might do so.

   a. The ages of students in a sixth-grade class.

   b. The ages of people in an elementary school.

   c. The ages of people eating in a family restaurant.

   d. The ages of people who watch football.

   e. The ages of runners in a marathon.

5. Jada drank 12 ounces of water from her bottle. This is 60% of the water the bottle holds.

   a. Write an equation to represent this situation. Explain the meaning of any variables you use.

   b. How much water does the bottle hold?

   (From Unit 6, Lesson 7.)

Lesson 9: Mean

Let's explore the mean of a data set and what it tells us.

9.1: Close to Four

Use the digits 0–9 to write an expression with a value as close as possible to 4. Each digit can be used only one time in the expression.

$$\left(\boxed{} + \boxed{} + \boxed{} + \boxed{}\right) \div 4$$

9.2: Spread Out and Share

1. The kittens in a room at an animal shelter are placed in 5 crates.

   a. The manager of the shelter wants the kittens distributed equally among the crates. How might that be done? How many kittens will end up in each crate?

   b. The number of kittens in each crate after they are equally distributed is called the **mean** number of kittens per crate, or the **average** number of kittens per crate. Explain how the expression $10 \div 5$ is related to the average.

c. Another room in the shelter has 6 crates. No two crates has the same number of kittens, and there is an average of 3 kittens per crate. Draw or describe at least two different arrangements of kittens that match this description.

2. Five servers were scheduled to work the number of hours shown. They decided to share the workload, so each one would work equal hours.

server A: 3   server B: 6   server C: 11   server D: 7   server E: 4

a. On the grid on the left, draw 5 bars whose heights represent the hours worked by servers A, B, C, D, and E.

b. Think about how you would rearrange the hours so that each server gets a fair share. Then, on the grid on the right, draw a new graph to represent the rearranged hours. Be prepared to explain your reasoning.

c. Based on your second drawing, what is the average or mean number of hours that the servers will work?

d. Explain why we can also find the mean by finding the value of the expression $31 \div 5$.

e. Which server will see the biggest change to work hours? Which server will see the least change?

iM KH

Are you ready for more?

Server F, working 7 hours, offers to join the group of five servers, sharing their workload. If server F joins, will the mean number of hours worked increase or decrease? Explain how you know.

9.3: Getting to School

For the past 12 school days, Mai has recorded how long her bus rides to school take in minutes. The times she recorded are shown in the table.

9	8	6	9	10	7	6	12	9	8	10	8

1. Find the mean for Mai's data. Show your reasoning.

2. In this situation, what does the mean tell us about Mai's trip to school?

3. For 5 days, Tyler has recorded how long his walks to school take in minutes. The mean for his data is 11 minutes. Without calculating, predict if each of the data sets shown could be Tyler's. Explain your reasoning.

   ○ data set A: 11, 8, 7, 9, 8

   ○ data set B: 12, 7, 13, 9, 14

   ○ data set C: 11, 20, 6, 9, 10

   ○ data set D: 8, 10, 9, 11, 11

4. Determine which data set is Tyler's. Explain how you know.

Lesson 9 Summary

Sometimes a general description of a distribution does not give enough information, and a more precise way to talk about center or spread would be more useful. The **mean**, or **average**, is a number we can use to summarize a distribution.

We can think about the mean in terms of "fair share" or "leveling out." That is, a mean can be thought of as a number that each member of a group would have if all the data values were combined and distributed equally among the members.

For example, suppose there are 5 bottles which have the following amounts of water: 1 liter, 4 liters, 2 liters, 3 liters, and 0 liters.

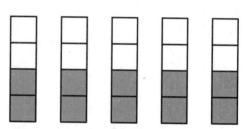

To find the mean, first we add up all of the values. We can think of this as putting all of the water together: $1 + 4 + 2 + 3 + 0 = 10$.

To find the "fair share," we divide the 10 liters equally into the 5 containers: $10 \div 5 = 2$.

Suppose the quiz scores of a student are 70, 90, 86, and 94. We can find the mean (or average) score by finding the sum of the scores ($70 + 90 + 86 + 94 = 340$) and dividing the sum by four ($340 \div 4 = 85$). We can then say that the student scored, on average, 85 points on the quizzes.

In general, to find the mean of a data set with n values, we add all of the values and divide the sum by n.

Glossary

- average
- mean

iM KH

Lesson 9 Practice Problems

1. A preschool teacher is rearranging four boxes of playing blocks so that each box contains an equal number of blocks. Currently Box 1 has 32 blocks, Box 2 has 18, Box 3 has 41, and Box 4 has 9.

   Select **all** the ways he could make each box have the same number of blocks.

   A. Remove all the blocks and make four equal piles of 25, then put each pile in one of the boxes.

   B. Remove 7 blocks from Box 1 and place them in Box 2.

   C. Remove 21 blocks from Box 3 and place them in Box 4.

   D. Remove 7 blocks from Box 1 and place them in Box 2, and remove 21 blocks from Box 3 and place them in Box 4.

   E. Remove 7 blocks from Box 1 and place them in Box 2, and remove 16 blocks from Box 3 and place them in Box 4.

2. In a round of mini-golf, Clare records the number of strokes it takes to hit the ball into the hole of each green.

2	3	1	4	5	2	3	4	3

   She said that, if she redistributed the strokes on different greens, she could tell that her average number of strokes per hole is 3. Explain how Clare is correct.

3. Three sixth-grade classes raised $25.50, $49.75, and $37.25 for their classroom libraries. They agreed to share the money raised equally. What is each class's equal share? Explain or show your reasoning.

4. In her English class, Mai's teacher gives 4 quizzes each worth 5 points. After 3 quizzes, she has the scores 4, 3, and 4. What does she need to get on the last quiz to have a mean score of 4? Explain or show your reasoning.

5. An earthworm farmer examined two containers of a certain species of earthworms so that he could learn about their lengths. He measured 25 earthworms in each container and recorded their lengths in millimeters.

   Here are histograms of the lengths for each container.

   a. Which container tends to have longer worms than the other container?

   b. For which container would 15 millimeters be a reasonable description of a typical length of the worms in the container?

   c. If length is related to age, which container had the most young worms?

   (From Unit 8, Lesson 7.)

6. Diego thinks that $x = 3$ is a solution to the equation $x^2 = 16$. Do you agree? Explain or show your reasoning.

   (From Unit 6, Lesson 15.)

iM KH

Lesson 10: Finding and Interpreting the Mean as the Balance Point

Let's look at another way to understand the mean of a data set.

10.1: Which One Doesn't Belong: Division

Which expression does not belong? Be prepared to explain your reasoning.

$$\frac{8+8+4+4}{4} \qquad \frac{10+10+4}{4} \qquad \frac{9+9+5+5}{4} \qquad \frac{6+6+6+6+6}{5}$$

10.2: Travel Times (Part 1)

Here is the data set from an earlier lesson showing how long it takes for Diego to walk to school, in minutes, over 5 days. The mean number of minutes is 11.

12   7   13   9   14

1. Represent Diego's data on a dot plot. Mark the location of the mean with a triangle.

2. The mean can also be seen as a **measure of center** that balances the points in a data set. If we find the distance between every point and the mean, add the distances on each side of the mean, and compare the two sums, we can see this balancing.

a. Record the distance between each point and 11 and its location relative to 11.

time in minutes	distance from 11	left of 11 or right of 11?
12		
7		
13		
9		
14		

b. Sum of distances left of 11:_____ Sum of distances right of 11:_____

What do you notice about the two sums?

3. Can another point that is *not* the mean produce similar sums of distances? Let's investigate whether 10 can produce similar sums as those of 11.

a. Complete the table with the distance of each data point from 10.

time in minutes	distance from 10	left of 10 or right of 10?
12		
7		
13		
9		
14		

b. Sum of distances left of 10:_____ Sum of distances right of 10:_____

What do you notice about the two sums?

4. Based on your work so far, explain why the mean can be considered a balance point for the data set.

iM KH

10.3: Travel Times (Part 2)

1. Here are dot plots showing how long Diego's trips to school took in minutes—which you studied earlier—and how long Andre's trips to school took in minutes. The dot plots include the means for each data set, marked by triangles.

Diego's travel time in minutes

Andre's travel time in minutes

   a. Which of the two data sets has a larger mean? In this context, what does a larger mean tell us?

   b. Which of the two data sets has larger sums of distances to the left and right of the mean? What do these sums tell us about the variation in Diego's and Andre's travel times?

2. Here is a dot plot showing lengths of Lin's trips to school.

travel time in minutes

   a. Calculate the mean of Lin's travel times.

b. Complete the table with the distance between each point and the mean as well whether the point is to the left or right of the mean.

time in minutes	distance from the mean	left or right of the mean?
22		
18		
11		
8		
11		

c. Find the sum of distances to the left of the mean and the sum of distances to the right of the mean.

d. Use your work to compare Lin's travel times to Andre's. What can you say about their average travel times? What about the variability in their travel times?

Lesson 10 Summary

The mean is often used as a **measure of center** of a distribution. This is because the mean of a distribution can be seen as the "balance point" for the distribution. Why is this a good way to think about the mean? Let's look at a very simple set of data on the number of cookies that each of eight friends baked:

19   20   20   21   21   22   22   23

iM KH

Here is a dot plot showing the data set.

number of cookies

The distribution shown is completely symmetrical. The mean number of cookies is 21, because $(19 + 20 + 20 + 21 + 21 + 22 + 22 + 23) \div 8 = 21$. If we mark the location of the mean on the dot plot, we can see that the data points could balance at 21.

In this plot, each point on either side of the mean has a mirror image. For example, the two points at 20 and the two at 22 are the same distance from 21, but each pair is located on either side of 21. We can think of them as balancing each other around 21.

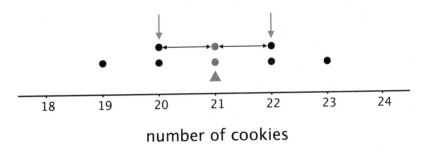

number of cookies

Similarly, the points at 19 and 23 are the same distance from 21 but are on either side of it. They, too, can be seen as balancing each other around 21.

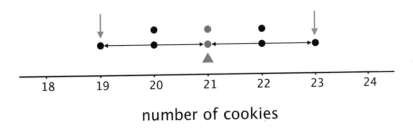

number of cookies

We can say that the distribution of the cookies has a center at 21 because that is its balance point, and that the eight friends, on average, baked 21 cookies.

Even when a distribution is not completely symmetrical, the distances of values below the mean, on the whole, balance the distances of values above the mean.

Glossary

- measure of center

Lesson 10 Practice Problems

1. On school days, Kiran walks to school. Here are the lengths of time, in minutes, for Kiran's walks on 5 school days:

   16   11   18   12   13

   a. Create a dot plot for Kiran's data.

   b. Without calculating, decide if 15 minutes would be a good estimate of the mean. If you think it is a good estimate, explain your reasoning. If not, give a better estimate and explain your reasoning.

   c. Calculate the mean for Kiran's data.

   d. In the table, record the distance of each data point from the mean and its location relative to the mean.

time in minutes	distance from the mean	left or right of the mean?
16		
11		
18		
12		
13		

   e. Calculate the sum of all distances to the left of the mean, then calculate the sum of distances to the right of the mean. Explain how these sums show that the mean is a balance point for the values in the data set.

2. Noah scored 20 points in a game. Mai's score was 30 points. The mean score for Noah, Mai, and Clare was 40 points. What was Clare's score? Explain or show your reasoning.

3. Compare the numbers using >, <, or =.

a. -2 _____ 3

a. 3 _____ -4

a. 7 _____ -11

b. |-12| _____ |15|

b. |15| _____ |-12|

b. -4 _____ |5|

(From Unit 7, Lesson 7.)

4.   a. Plot $\frac{2}{3}$ and $\frac{3}{4}$ on a number line.

b. Is $\frac{2}{3} < \frac{3}{4}$, or is $\frac{3}{4} < \frac{2}{3}$? Explain how you know.

(From Unit 7, Lesson 3.)

5. Select **all** the expressions that represent the total area of the large rectangle.

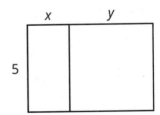

A. $5(x + y)$

B. $5 + xy$

C. $5x + 5y$

D. $2(5 + x + y)$

E. $5xy$

(From Unit 6, Lesson 10.)

Lesson 11: Variability and MAD

Let's study distances between data points and the mean and see what they tell us.

11.1: Shooting Hoops (Part 1)

Elena, Jada, and Lin enjoy playing basketball during recess. Lately, they have been practicing free throws. They record the number of baskets they make out of 10 attempts. Here are their data sets for 12 school days.

Elena

| 4 | 5 | 1 | 6 | 9 | 7 | 2 | 8 | 3 | 3 | 5 | 7 |

Jada

| 2 | 4 | 5 | 4 | 6 | 6 | 4 | 7 | 3 | 4 | 8 | 7 |

Lin

| 3 | 6 | 6 | 4 | 5 | 5 | 3 | 5 | 4 | 6 | 6 | 7 |

1. Calculate the mean number of baskets each player made, and compare the means. What do you notice?

2. What do the means tell us in this context?

iM KH

11.2: Shooting Hoops (Part 2)

Here are the dot plots showing the number of baskets Elena, Jada, and Lin each made over 12 school days.

1. On each dot plot, mark the location of the mean with a triangle (Δ). Then, contrast the dot plot distributions. Write 2–3 sentences to describe the shape and spread of each distribution.

number of baskets Elena made

number of baskets Jada made

number of baskets Lin made

2. Discuss the following questions with your group. Explain your reasoning.

   a. Would you say that all three students play equally well?

   b. Would you say that all three students play equally consistently?

   c. If you could choose one player to be on your basketball team based on their records, who would you choose?

11.3: Shooting Hoops (Part 3)

The tables show Elena, Jada, and Lin's basketball data from an earlier activity. Recall that the mean of Elena's data, as well as that of Jada and Lin's data, was 5.

1. Record the distance between each of Elena's scores and the mean.

Elena	4	5	1	6	9	7	2	8	3	3	5	7
distance from 5	1			1								

Now find *the average of the distances* in the table. Show your reasoning and round your answer to the nearest tenth.

This value is the **mean absolute deviation (MAD)** of Elena's data.

Elena's MAD: _____

2. Find the mean absolute deviation of Jada's data. Round it to the nearest tenth.

Jada	2	4	5	4	6	6	4	7	3	4	8	7
distance from 5												

Jada's MAD: _____

iM KH

3. Find the mean absolute deviation of Lin's data. Round it to the nearest tenth.

Lin	3	6	6	4	5	5	3	5	4	6	6	7
distance from 5												

Lin's MAD: _____

4. Compare the MADs and dot plots of the three students' data. Do you see a relationship between each student's MAD and the distribution on her dot plot? Explain your reasoning.

number of baskets Elena made

number of baskets Jada made

number of baskets Lin made

Are you ready for more?

Invent another data set that also has a mean of 5 but has a MAD greater than 2. Remember, the values in the data set must be whole numbers from 0 to 10.

11.4: Game of 22

Your teacher will give your group a deck of cards. Shuffle the cards, and put the deck face down on the playing surface.

- To play: Draw 3 cards and add up the values. An ace is a 1. A jack, queen, and king are each worth 10. Cards 2–10 are each worth their face value. If your sum is anything other than 22 (either above or below 22), say: "My sum deviated from 22 by ___ ," or "My sum was off from 22 by ___ ."

- To keep score: Record each sum and each distance from 22 in the table. After five rounds, calculate the average of the distances. The player with the lowest average distance from 22 wins the game.

player A	round 1	round 2	round 3	round 4	round 5
sum of cards					
distance from 22					

Average distance from 22: _____

player B	round 1	round 2	round 3	round 4	round 5
sum of cards					
distance from 22					

Average distance from 22: _____

player C	round 1	round 2	round 3	round 4	round 5
sum of cards					
distance from 22					

Average distance from 22: _____

Whose average distance from 22 is the smallest? Who won the game?

iM KH

Lesson 11 Summary

We use the mean of a data set as a measure of center of its distribution, but two data sets with the same mean could have very different distributions.

This dot plot shows the weights, in grams, of 22 cookies.

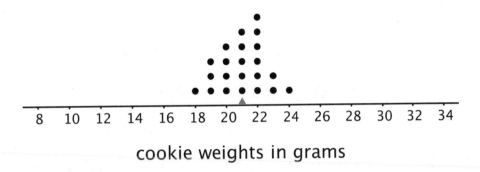

cookie weights in grams

The mean weight is 21 grams. All the weights are within 3 grams of the mean, and most of them are even closer. These cookies are all fairly close in weight.

This dot plot shows the weights, in grams, of a different set of 30 cookies.

cookie weights in grams

The mean weight for this set of cookies is also 21 grams, but some cookies are half that weight and others are one-and-a-half times that weight. There is a lot more variability in the weight.

There is a number we can use to describe how far away, or how spread out, data points generally are from the mean. This *measure of spread* is called the **mean absolute deviation (MAD)**.

Here the MAD tells us how far cookie weights typically are from 21 grams. To find the MAD, we find the distance between each data value and the mean, and then calculate the mean of those distances.

For instance, the point that represents 18 grams is 3 units away from the mean of 21 grams. We can find the distance between each point and the mean of 21 grams and organize the distances into a table, as shown.

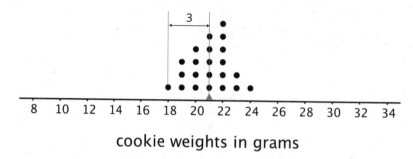

cookie weights in grams

weight in grams	18	19	19	19	20	20	20	20	21	21	21	21	21	22	22	22	22	22	22	23	23	24
distance from mean	3	2	2	2	1	1	1	1	0	0	0	0	0	1	1	1	1	1	1	2	2	3

The values in the first row of the table are the cookie weights for the first set of cookies. Their mean, 21 grams, is the *mean of the cookie weights*.

The values in the second row of the table are the *distances* between the values in the first row and 21. The mean of these distances is the *MAD of the cookie weights*.

What can we learn from the averages of these distances once they are calculated?

- In the first set of cookies, the distances are all between 0 and 3. The MAD is 1.2 grams, which tells us that the cookie weights are typically within 1.2 grams of 21 grams. We could say that a typical cookie weighs between 19.8 and 22.2 grams.

- In the second set of cookies, the distances are all between 0 and 13. The MAD is 5.6 grams, which tells us that the cookie weights are typically within 5.6 grams of 21 grams. We could say a typical cookie weighs between 15.4 and 26.6 grams.

The MAD is also called a *measure of the variability* of the distribution. In these examples, it is easy to see that a higher MAD suggests a distribution that is more spread out, showing more variability.

Glossary

- mean absolute deviation (MAD)

iM KH

Lesson 11 Practice Problems

1. Han recorded the number of pages that he read each day for five days. The dot plot shows his data.

number of pages

   a. Is 30 pages a good estimate of the mean number of pages that Han read each day? Explain your reasoning.

   b. Find the mean number of pages that Han read during the five days. Draw a triangle to mark the mean on the dot plot.

   c. Use the dot plot and the mean to complete the table.

number of pages	distance from mean	left or right of mean
25		left
28		
32		
36		
42		

   d. Calculate the mean absolute deviation (MAD) of the data. Explain or show your reasoning.

2. Ten sixth-grade students recorded the amounts of time each took to travel to school. The dot plot shows their travel times.

travel time in minutes

The mean travel time for these students is approximately 9 minutes. The MAD is approximately 4.2 minutes.

   a. Which number of minutes—9 or 4.2—is a typical amount of time for the ten sixth-grade students to travel to school? Explain your reasoning.

   b. Based on the mean and MAD, Jada believes that travel times between 5 and 13 minutes are common for this group. Do you agree? Explain your reasoning.

   c. A different group of ten sixth-grade students also recorded their travel times to school. Their mean travel time was also 9 minutes, but the MAD was about 7 minutes. What could the dot plot of this second data set be? Describe or draw how it might look.

3. In an archery competition, scores for each round are calculated by averaging the distance of 3 arrows from the center of the target.

   An archer has a mean distance of 1.6 inches and a MAD distance of 1.3 inches in the first round. In the second round, the archer's arrows are farther from the center but are more consistent. What values for the mean and MAD would fit this description for the second round? Explain your reasoning.

Lesson 12: Using Mean and MAD to Make Comparisons

Let's use mean and MAD to describe and compare distributions.

12.1: Number Talk: Decimal Division

Find the value of each expression mentally.

$42 \div 12$

$2.4 \div 12$

$44.4 \div 12$

$46.8 \div 12$

12.2: Which Player Would You Choose?

1. Andre and Noah joined Elena, Jada, and Lin in recording their basketball scores. They all recorded their scores in the same way: the number of baskets made out of 10 attempts. Each collected 12 data points.

   ○ Andre's mean number of baskets was 5.25, and his MAD was 2.6.

   ○ Noah's mean number of baskets was also 5.25, but his MAD was 1.

Here are two dot plots that represent the two data sets. The triangle indicates the location of the mean.

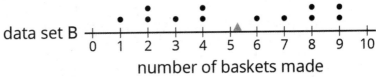

number of baskets made

   a. Without calculating, decide which dot plot represents Andre's data and which represents Noah's. Explain how you know.

b. If you were the captain of a basketball team and could use one more player on your team, would you choose Andre or Noah? Explain your reasoning.

2. An eighth-grade student decided to join Andre and Noah and kept track of his scores. His data set is shown here. The mean number of baskets he made is 6.

eighth-grade student	6	5	4	7	6	5	7	8	5	6	5	8
distance from 6												

a. Calculate the MAD. Show your reasoning.

b. Draw a dot plot to represent his data and mark the location of the mean with a triangle (Δ).

c. Compare the eighth-grade student's mean and MAD to Noah's mean and MAD. What do you notice?

d. Compare their dot plots. What do you notice about the distributions?

e. What can you say about the two players' shooting accuracy and consistency?

iM KH

Are you ready for more?

Invent a data set with a mean of 7 and a MAD of 1.

12.3: Swimmers Over the Years

In 1984, the mean age of swimmers on the U.S. women's swimming team was 18.2 years and the MAD was 2.2 years. In 2016, the mean age of the swimmers was 22.8 years, and the MAD was 3 years.

1. How has the average age of the women on the U.S. swimming team changed from 1984 to 2016? Explain your reasoning.

2. Are the swimmers on the 1984 team closer in age to one another than the swimmers on the 2016 team are to one another? Explain your reasoning.

3. Here are dot plots showing the ages of the women on the U.S. swimming team in 1984 and in 2016. Use them to make two other comments about how the women's swimming team has changed over the years.

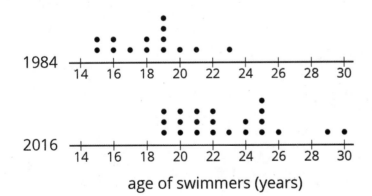

age of swimmers (years)

Lesson 12 Summary

Sometimes two distributions have different means but the same MAD.

Pugs and beagles are two different dog breeds. The dot plot shows two sets of weight data—one for pugs and the other for beagles.

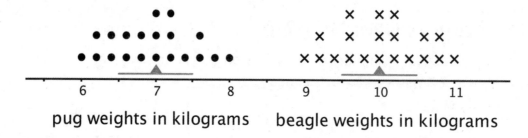

pug weights in kilograms   beagle weights in kilograms

- The mean weight for pugs is 7 kilograms, and the MAD is 0.5 kilogram.

- The mean weight for beagles is 10 kilograms, and the MAD is 0.5 kilogram.

We can say that, in general, the beagles are heavier than the pugs. A typical weight for the beagles in this group is about 3 kilograms heavier than a typical weight for the pugs.

The variability of pug weights, however, is about the same as the variability of beagle weights. In other words, the weights of pugs and the weights of beagles are equally spread out.

Lesson 12 Practice Problems

1. The dot plots show the amounts of time that ten U.S. students and ten Australian students took to get to school.

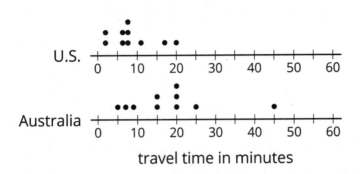

Which statement is true about the MAD of the Australian data set?

A. It is significantly less than the MAD of the U.S. data set.

B. It is exactly equal to the MAD of the U.S. data set.

C. It is approximately equal to the MAD of the U.S. data set.

D. It is significantly greater than the MAD of the U.S. data set.

2. The dot plots show the amounts of time that ten South African students and ten Australian students took to get to school. Without calculating, answer the questions.

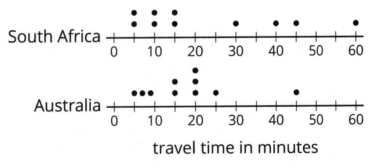

a. Which data set has the smaller mean? Explain your reasoning.

b. Which data set has the smaller MAD? Explain your reasoning.

c. What does a smaller mean tell us in this context?

d. What does a smaller MAD tell us in this context?

3. Two high school basketball teams have identical records of 15 wins and 2 losses. Sunnyside High School's mean score is 50 points and its MAD is 4 points. Shadyside High School's mean score is 60 points and its MAD is 15 points.

   Lin read the records of each team's score. She likes the team that had nearly the same score for every game it played. Which team do you think Lin likes? Explain your reasoning.

4. Jada thinks the perimeter of this rectangle can be represented with the expression $a + a + b + b$. Andre thinks it can be represented with $2a + 2b$. Do you agree with either of them? Explain your reasoning.

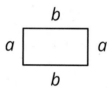

(From Unit 6, Lesson 8.)

5. Draw a number line.

   a. Plot and label three numbers between -2 and -8 (not including -2 and -8).

   b. Use the numbers you plotted and the symbols $<$ and $>$ to write three inequality statements.

(From Unit 7, Lesson 3.)

6. Adult elephant seals generally weigh about 5,500 pounds. If you weighed 5 elephant seals, would you expect each seal to weigh exactly 5,500 pounds? Explain your reasoning.

(From Unit 8, Lesson 2.)

iM KH

Lesson 13: Median

Let's explore the median of a data set and what it tells us.

13.1: The Plot of the Story

1. Here are two dot plots and two stories. Match each story with a dot plot that could represent it. Be prepared to explain your reasoning.

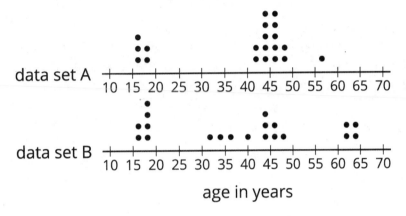

data set A

data set B

age in years

- Twenty people—high school students, teachers, and invited guests—attended a rehearsal for a high school musical. The mean age was 38.5 years and the MAD was 16.5 years.

- High school soccer team practice is usually watched by supporters of the players. One evening, twenty people watched the team practice. The mean age was 38.5 years and the MAD was 12.7 years.

2. Another evening, twenty people watched the soccer team practice. The mean age was similar to that from the first evening, but the MAD was greater (about 20 years). Make a dot plot that could illustrate the distribution of ages in this story.

age in years

13.2: Siblings in the House

Here is data that shows the numbers of siblings of ten students in Tyler's class.

| 1 | 0 | 2 | 1 | 7 | 0 | 2 | 0 | 1 | 10 |

1. Represent the data shown with a dot plot.

2. Without making any calculations, estimate the center of the data based on your dot plot. What is a typical number of siblings for these sixth-grade students? Mark the location of that number on your dot plot.

3. Find the mean. Show your reasoning.

4.   a. How does the mean compare to the value that you marked on the dot plot as a typical number of siblings? (Is it a little larger, a lot larger, exactly the same, a little smaller, or a lot smaller than your estimate?)

      b. Do you think the mean summarizes the data set well? Explain your reasoning.

Are you ready for more?

Invent a data set with a mean that is significantly lower than what you would consider a typical value for the data set.

13.3: Finding the Middle

1. Your teacher will give you an index card. Write your first and last names on the card. Then record the total number of letters in your name. After that, pause for additional instructions from your teacher.

2. Here is the data set on numbers of siblings from an earlier activity.

    1   0   2   1   7   0   2   0   1   10

    a. Sort the data from least to greatest, and then find the **median**.

    b. In this situation, do you think the median is a good measure of a typical number of siblings for this group? Explain your reasoning.

3. Here is the dot plot showing the travel time, in minutes, of Elena's bus rides to school.

travel time in minutes

    a. Find the median travel time. Be prepared to explain your reasoning.

    b. What does the median tell us in this context?

Lesson 13 Summary

The **median** is another measure of center of a distribution. It is the middle value in a data set when values are listed in order. Half of the values in a data set are less than or equal to the median, and half of the values are greater than or equal to the median.

To find the median, we order the data values from least to greatest and find the number in the middle.

Suppose we have 5 dogs whose weights, in pounds, are shown in the table. The median weight for this group of dogs is 32 pounds because three dogs weigh less than or equal to 32 pounds and three dogs weigh greater than or equal to 32 pounds.

20	25	32	40	55

Now suppose we have 6 cats whose weights, in pounds, are as shown in the table. Notice that there are *two* values in the middle: 7 and 8.

4	6	7	8	10	10

The median weight must be between 7 and 8 pounds, because half of the cats weigh less or equal to 7 pounds and half of the cats weigh greater than or equal to 8 pounds.

In general, when we have an even number of values, we take the number exactly in between the two middle values. In this case, the median cat weight is 7.5 pounds because $(7 + 8) \div 2 = 7.5$.

Glossary

- median

iM KH

Lesson 13 Practice Problems

1. Here is data that shows a student's scores for 10 rounds of a video game.

   | 130 | 150 | 120 | 170 | 130 | 120 | 160 | 160 | 190 | 140 |

   What is the median score?

   A. 125

   B. 145

   C. 147

   D. 150

2. When he sorts the class's scores on the last test, the teacher notices that exactly 12 students scored better than Clare and exactly 12 students scored worse than Clare. Does this mean that Clare's score on the test is the median? Explain your reasoning.

3. The medians of the following dot plots are 6, 12, 13, and 15, but not in that order. Match each dot plot with its median.

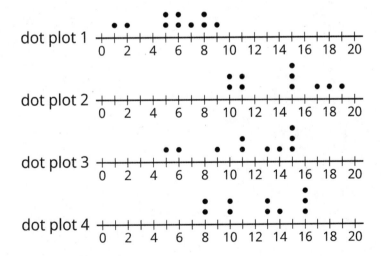

4. Invent a data set with five numbers that has a mean of 10 and a median of 12.

5. Ten sixth-grade students reported the hours of sleep they get on nights before a school day. Their responses are recorded in the dot plot.

hours of sleep

Looking at the dot plot, Lin estimated the mean number of hours of sleep to be 8.5 hours. Noah's estimate was 7.5 hours. Diego's estimate was 6.5 hours.

Which estimate do you think is best? Explain how you know.

(From Unit 8, Lesson 10.)

iM KH

6. In one study of wild bears, researchers measured the weights, in pounds, of 143 wild bears that ranged in age from newborn to 15 years old. The data were used to make this histogram.

a. What can you say about the heaviest bear in this group?

weight in pounds

b. What is a typical weight for the bears in this group?

c. Do more than half of the bears in this group weigh less than 250 pounds?

d. If weight is related to age, with older bears tending to have greater body weights, would you say that there were more old bears or more young bears in the group? Explain your reasoning.

(From Unit 8, Lesson 8.)

Lesson 14: Comparing Mean and Median

Let's compare the mean and median of data sets.

14.1: Heights of Presidents

Here are two dot plots. The first dot plot shows the heights of the first 22 U.S. presidents. The second dot plot shows the heights of the next 22 presidents.

height in centimeters

Based on the two dot plots, decide if you agree or disagree with each of the following statements. Be prepared to explain your reasoning.

1. The median height of the first 22 presidents is 178 centimeters.

2. The mean height of the first 22 presidents is about 183 centimeters.

3. A typical height for a president in the second group is about 182 centimeters.

4. U.S. presidents have become taller over time.

5. The heights of the first 22 presidents are more alike than the heights of the second 22 presidents.

6. The MAD of the second data set is greater than the MAD of the first set.

iM KH

14.2: The Tallest and the Smallest in the World

Your teacher will provide the height data for your class. Use the data to complete the following questions.

1. Find the mean height of your class in centimeters.

2. Find the median height in centimeters. Show your reasoning.

3. Suppose that the world's tallest adult, who is 251 centimeters tall, joined your class.

   a. Discuss the following questions with your group and explain your reasoning.

      ■ How would the mean height of the class change?

      ■ How would the median height change?

   b. Find the new mean.

   c. Find the new median.

   d. Which measure of center—the mean or the median—changed more when this new person joined the class? Explain why the value of one measure changed more than the other.

4. The world's smallest adult is 63 centimeters tall. Suppose that the world's tallest and smallest adults both joined your class.

    a. Discuss the following questions with your group and explain your reasoning.

        ■ How would the mean height of the class change from the original mean?

        ■ How would the median height change from the original median?

    b. Find the new mean.

    c. Find the new median.

    d. How did the measures of center—the mean and the median—change when these two people joined the class? Explain why the values of the mean and median changed the way they did.

14.3: Mean or Median?

1. Your teacher will give you six cards. Each has either a dot plot or a histogram. Sort the cards into *two* piles based on the distributions shown. Be prepared to explain your reasoning.

2. Discuss your sorting decisions with another group. Did you have the same cards in each pile? If so, did you use the same sorting categories? If not, how are your categories different?

Pause here for a class discussion.

3. Use the information on the cards to answer the following questions.

   a. Card A: What is a typical age of the dogs being treated at the animal clinic?

   b. Card B: What is a typical number of people in the Irish households?

   c. Card C: What is a typical travel time for the New Zealand students?

   d. Card D: Would 15 years old be a good description of a typical age of the people who attended the birthday party?

   e. Card E: Is 15 minutes or 24 minutes a better description of a typical time it takes the students in South Africa to get to school?

   f. Card F: Would 21.3 years old be a good description of a typical age of the people who went on a field trip to Washington, D.C.?

4. How did you decide which measure of center to use for the dot plots on Cards A–C? What about for those on Cards D–F?

Are you ready for more?

Most teachers use the mean to calculate a student's final grade, based on that student's scores on tests, quizzes, homework, projects, and other graded assignments.

Diego thinks that the median might be a better way to measure how well a student did in a course. Do you agree with Diego? Explain your reasoning.

Lesson 14 Summary

Both the mean and the median are ways of measuring the center of a distribution. They tell us slightly different things, however.

The dot plot shows the weights of 30 cookies. The mean weight is 21 grams (marked with a triangle). The median weight is 20.5 grams (marked with a diamond).

cookie weights in grams

The mean tells us that if the weights of all cookies were distributed so that each one weighed the same, that weight would be 21 grams. We could also think of 21 grams as a balance point for the weights of all of the cookies in the set.

The median tells us that half of the cookies weigh more than 20.5 grams and half weigh less than 20.5 grams. In this case, both the mean and the median could describe a typical cookie weight because they are fairly close to each other and to most of the data points.

Here is a different set of 30 cookies. It has the same mean weight as the first set, but the median weight is 23 grams.

cookie weights in grams

In this case, the median is closer to where most of the data points are clustered and is therefore a better measure of center for this distribution. That is, it is a better description of a typical cookie weight. The mean weight is influenced (in this case, pulled down) by a handful of much smaller cookies, so it is farther away from most data points.

In general, when a distribution is symmetrical or approximately symmetrical, the mean and median values are close. But when a distribution is not roughly symmetrical, the two values tend to be farther apart.

iM KH

Lesson 14 Practice Problems

1. Here is a dot plot that shows the ages of teachers at a school.

Which of these statements is true of the data set shown in the dot plot?

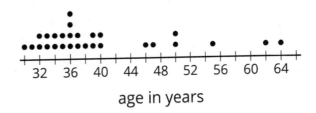

age in years

A. The mean is less than the median.

B. The mean is approximately equal to the median.

C. The mean is greater than the median.

D. The mean cannot be determined.

2. Priya asked each of five friends to attempt to throw a ball in a trash can until they succeeded. She recorded the number of unsuccessful attempts made by each friend as: 1, 8, 6, 2, 4. Priya made a mistake: The 8 in the data set should have been 18.

How would changing the 8 to 18 affect the mean and median of the data set?

A. The mean would decrease and the median would not change.

B. The mean would increase and the median would not change.

C. The mean would decrease and the median would increase.

D. The mean would increase and the median would increase.

3. In his history class, Han's homework scores are:

100   100   100   100   95   100   90   100   0

The history teacher uses the mean to calculate the grade for homework. Write an argument for Han to explain why median would be a better measure to use for his homework grades.

4. The dot plots show how much time, in minutes, students in a class took to complete each of five different tasks. Select **all** the dot plots of tasks for which the mean time is approximately equal to the median time.

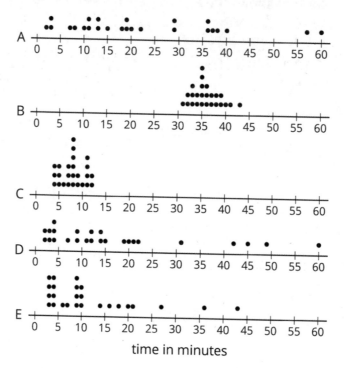

time in minutes

5. Zookeepers recorded the ages, weights, genders, and heights of the 10 pandas at their zoo. Write two statistical questions that could be answered using these data sets.

(From Unit 8, Lesson 2.)

6. Here is a set of coordinates. Draw and label an appropriate pair of axes and plot the points. $A = (1, 0)$, $B = (0, 0.5)$, $C = (4, 3.5)$, $D = (1.5, 0.5)$

(From Unit 7, Lesson 12.)

iM KH

Lesson 15: Quartiles and Interquartile Range

Let's look at other measures for describing distributions.

15.1: Notice and Wonder: Two Parties

Here are dot plots that show the ages of people at two different parties. The mean of each distribution is marked with a triangle.

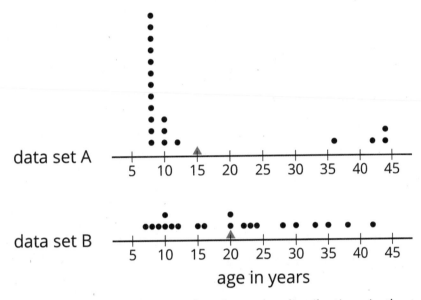

What do you notice and what do you wonder about the distributions in the two dot plots?

15.2: The Five-Number Summary

Here are the ages of the people at one party, listed from least to greatest.

7	8	9	10	10	11	12	15
16	20	20	22	23	24	28	30
33	35	38	42				

1. a. Find the median of the data set and label it "50th percentile." This splits the data into an upper half and a lower half.

    b. Find the middle value of the *lower* half of the data, without including the median. Label this value "25th percentile."

    c. Find the middle value of the *upper* half of the data, without including the median. Label this value "75th percentile."

2. You have split the data set into four pieces. Each of the three values that split the data is called a **quartile**.

    ○ We call the 25th percentile the *first quartile*. Write "Q1" next to that number.
    ○ The median can be called the *second quartile*. Write "Q2" next to that number.
    ○ We call the 75th percentile the *third quartile*. Write "Q3" next to that number.

3. Label the lowest value in the set "minimum" and the greatest value "maximum."

4. The values you have identified make up the *five-number summary* for the data set. Record them here.

   minimum: _____   Q1: _____   Q2: _____   Q3: _____   maximum: _____

iM KH

5. The median of this data set is 20. This tells us that half of the people at the party were 20 years old or younger, and the other half were 20 or older. What do each of these other values tell us about the ages of the people at the party?

  a. the third quartile

  b. the minimum

  c. the maximum

Are you ready for more?

There was another party where 21 people attended. Here is the five-number summary of their ages.

minimum: _5_   Q1: _6_   Q2: _27_   Q3: _32_   maximum: _60_

1. Do you think this party had more children or fewer children than the earlier one? Explain your reasoning.

2. Were there more children or adults at this party? Explain your reasoning.

15.3: Range and Interquartile Range

1. Here is a dot plot that shows the lengths of Elena's bus rides to school, over 12 days.

travel time in minutes

Write the five-number summary for this data set. Show your reasoning.

2. The **range** is one way to describe the *spread* of values in a data set. It is the difference between the maximum and minimum. What is the range of Elena's travel times?

3. Another way to describe the spread of values in a data set is the **interquartile range (IQR)**. It is the difference between the upper quartile and the lower quartile.

    a. What is the interquartile range (IQR) of Elena's travel times?

    b. What fraction of the data values are between the lower and upper quartiles?

4. Here are two more dot plots.

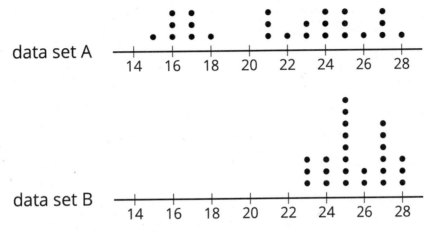

data set A

data set B

Without doing any calculations, predict:

   a. Which data set has the smaller range?

   b. Which data set has the smaller IQR?

5. Check your predictions by calculating the range and IQR for the data in each dot plot.

Lesson 15 Summary

Earlier we learned that the mean is a measure of the center of a distribution and the MAD is a measure of the variability (or spread) that goes with the mean. There is also a measure of spread that goes with the median. It is called the interquartile range (IQR).

Finding the IQR involves splitting a data set into fourths. Each of the three values that splits the data into fourths is called a **quartile**.

- The median, or second quartile (Q2), splits the data into two halves.
- The first quartile (Q1) is the middle value of the lower half of the data.
- The third quartile (Q3) is the middle value of the upper half of the data.

For example, here is a data set with 11 values.

12	19	20	21	22	33	34	35	40	40	49
		Q1			Q2			Q3		

- The median is 33.
- The first quartile is 20. It is the median of the numbers less than 33.
- The third quartile 40. It is the median of the numbers greater than 33.

The difference between the maximum and minimum values of a data set is the **range**. The difference between Q3 and Q1 is the **interquartile range (IQR)**. Because the distance between Q1 and Q3 includes the middle two-fourths of the distribution, the values between those two quartiles are sometimes called the *middle half of the data.*

The bigger the IQR, the more spread out the middle half of the data values are. The smaller the IQR, the closer together the middle half of the data values are. This is why we can use the IQR as a measure of spread.

A *five-number summary* can be used to summarize a distribution. It includes the minimum, first quartile, median, third quartile, and maximum of the data set. For the previous example, the five-number summary is 12, 20, 33, 40, and 49. These numbers are marked with diamonds on the dot plot.

Different data sets can have the same five-number summary. For instance, here is another data set with the same minimum, maximum, and quartiles as the previous example.

Glossary

- interquartile range (IQR)
- quartile
- range

iᴍ **KH**

Lesson 15 Practice Problems

1. Suppose that there are 20 numbers in a data set and that they are all different.

   a. How many of the values in this data set are between the first quartile and the third quartile?

   b. How many of the values in this data set are between the first quartile and the median?

2. In a word game, 1 letter is worth 1 point. This dot plot shows the scores for 20 common words.

word value in points

   a. What is the median score?

   b. What is the first quartile (Q1)?

   c. What is the third quartile (Q3)?

   d. What is the interquartile range (IQR)?

3. Mai and Priya each played 10 games of bowling and recorded the scores. Mai's median score was 120, and her IQR was 5. Priya's median score was 118, and her IQR was 15. Whose scores probably had less variability? Explain how you know.

4. Here are five dot plots that show the amounts of time that ten sixth-grade students in five countries took to get to school. Match each dot plot with the appropriate median and IQR.

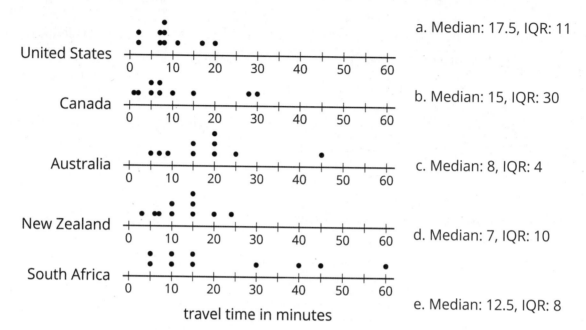

a. Median: 17.5, IQR: 11

b. Median: 15, IQR: 30

c. Median: 8, IQR: 4

d. Median: 7, IQR: 10

e. Median: 12.5, IQR: 8

travel time in minutes

5. Draw and label an appropriate pair of axes and plot the points. $A = (10, 50)$, $B = (30, 25)$, $C = (0, 30)$, $D = (20, 35)$

(From Unit 7, Lesson 12.)

6. There are 20 pennies in a jar. If 16% of the coins in the jar are pennies, how many coins are there in the jar?

(From Unit 6, Lesson 7.)

iM KH

Lesson 16: Box Plots

Let's explore how box plots can help us summarize distributions.

16.1: Notice and Wonder: Puppy Weights

Here are the birth weights, in ounces, of all the puppies born at a kennel in the past month.

13	14	15	15	16	16	16	16
17	17	17	17	17	17	17	18
18	18	18	18	18	18	18	19
20							

What do you notice and wonder about the distribution of the puppy weights?

16.2: Human Box Plot

Your teacher will give you the data on the lengths of names of students in your class. Write the five-number summary by finding the data set's minimum, Q1, Q2, Q3, and the maximum.

Pause for additional instructions from your teacher.

16.3: Studying Blinks

Twenty people participated in a study about blinking. The number of times each person blinked while watching a video for one minute was recorded. The data values are shown here, in order from smallest to largest.

3	6	8	11	11	13	14	14
14	14	16	18	20	20	20	22
24	32	36	51				

1. a. Use the grid and axis to make a dot plot of this data set.

number of blinks

b. Find the median (Q2) and mark its location on the dot plot.

c. Find the first quartile (Q1) and the third quartile (Q3). Mark their locations on the dot plot.

d. What are the minimum and maximum values?

2. A **box plot** can be used to represent the five-number summary graphically. Let's draw a box plot for the number-of-blinks data. On the grid, *above* the dot plot:

a. Draw a box that extends from the first quartile (Q1) to the third quartile (Q3). Label the quartiles.

b. At the median (Q2), draw a vertical line from the top of the box to the bottom of the box. Label the median.

c. From the left side of the box (Q1), draw a horizontal line (a whisker) that extends to the minimum of the data set. On the right side of the box (Q3), draw a similar line that extends to the maximum of the data set.

iM KH

3. You have now created a box plot to represent the number of blinks data. What fraction of the data values are represented by each of these elements of the box plot?

    a. The left whisker

    b. The box

    c. The right whisker

Are you ready for more?

Suppose there were some errors in the data set: the smallest value should have been 6 instead of 3, and the largest value should have been 41 instead of 51. Determine if any part of the five-number summary would change. If you think so, describe how it would change. If not, explain how you know.

Lesson 16 Summary

A **box plot** represents the five-number summary of a data set.

It shows the first quartile (Q1) and the third quartile (Q3) as the left and right sides of a rectangle or a box. The median (Q2) is shown as a vertical segment inside the box. On the left side, a horizontal line segment—a "whisker"—extends from Q1 to the minimum value. On the right, a whisker extends from Q3 to the maximum value.

The rectangle in the middle represents the middle half of the data. Its width is the IQR. The whiskers represent the bottom quarter and top quarter of the data set.

Earlier we saw dot plots representing the weights of pugs and beagles. The box plots for these data sets are shown above the corresponding dot plots.

pug weights in kilograms   beagle weights in kilograms

We can tell from the box plots that, in general, the pugs in the group are lighter than the beagles: the median weight of pugs is 7 kilograms and the median weight of beagles is 10 kilograms. Because the two box plots are on the same scale and the rectangles have similar widths, we can also tell that the IQRs for the two breeds are very similar. This suggests that the variability in the beagle weights is very similar to the variability in the pug weights.

Glossary

- box plot

Lesson 16 Practice Problems

1. Each student in a class recorded how many books they read during the summer. Here is a box plot that summarizes their data.

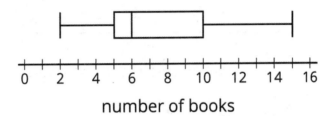

number of books

   a. What is the greatest number of books read by a student in this group?

   b. What is the median number of books read by the students?

   c. What is the interquartile range (IQR)?

2. Use this five-number summary to draw a box plot. All values are in seconds.

   ○ Minimum: 40

   ○ First quartile (Q1): 45

   ○ Median: 48

   ○ Third quartile (Q3): 50

   ○ Maximum: 60

3. The data shows the number of hours per week that each of 13 seventh-grade students spent doing homework. Create a box plot to summarize the data.

3	10	12	4	7	9	5	5
11	11	5	12	11			

4. The box plot displays the data on the response times of 100 mice to seeing a flash of light. How many mice are represented by the rectangle between 0.5 and 1 second?

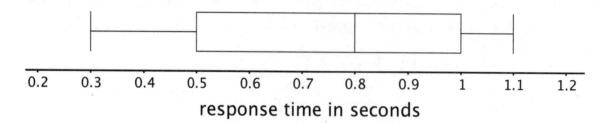

response time in seconds

5. Here is a dot plot that represents a data set. Explain why the mean of the data set is greater than its median.

(From Unit 8, Lesson 14.)

6. Jada earns money from babysitting, walking her neighbor's dogs, and running errands for her aunt. Every four weeks, she combines her earnings and divides them into three equal parts—one for spending, one for saving, and one for donating to a charity. Jada donated $26.00 of her earnings from the past four weeks to charity.

   How much could she have earned from each job? Make two lists of how much she could have earned from the three jobs during the past four weeks.

   (From Unit 8, Lesson 9.)

iM KH

Lesson 17: Using Box Plots

Let's use box plots to make comparisons.

17.1: Hours of Slumber

Ten sixth-grade students were asked how much sleep, in hours, they usually get on a school night. Here is the five-number summary of their responses.

- Minimum: 5 hours
- Median: 7.5 hours
- Maximum: 9 hours
- First quartile: 7 hours
- Third quartile: 8 hours

1. On the grid, draw a box plot for this five-number summary.

hours of sleep

2. What questions could be answered by looking at this box plot?

17.2: Info Gap: Sea Turtles

Your teacher will give you either a Problem Card or a Data Card about sea turtles that nest on the Outer Banks of North Carolina. Do not show or read your card to your partner.

If your teacher gives you the *problem card*:

1. Silently read your card and think about what information you need to be able to answer the question.

2. Ask your partner for the specific information that you need.

3. Explain how you are using the information to solve the problem.

   Continue to ask questions until you have enough information to solve the problem.

4. Share the *problem card* and solve the problem independently.

5. Read the *data card* and discuss your reasoning.

If your teacher gives you the *data card*:

1. Silently read your card.

2. Ask your partner *"What specific information do you need?"* and wait for them to *ask* for information.

   If your partner asks for information that is not on the card, do not do the calculations for them. Tell them you don't have that information.

3. Before sharing the information, ask *"Why do you need that information?"* Listen to your partner's reasoning and ask clarifying questions.

4. Read the *problem card* and solve the problem independently.

5. Share the *data card* and discuss your reasoning.

Pause here so your teacher can review your work. Ask your teacher for a new set of cards and repeat the activity, trading roles with your partner.

iM KH

17.3: Paper Planes

Andre, Lin, and Noah each designed and built a paper airplane. They launched each plane several times and recorded the distance of each flight in yards.

Andre

| 25 | 26 | 27 | 27 | 27 | 28 | 28 | 28 | 29 | 30 | 30 |

Lin

| 20 | 20 | 21 | 24 | 26 | 28 | 28 | 29 | 29 | 30 | 32 |

Noah

| 13 | 14 | 15 | 18 | 19 | 20 | 21 | 23 | 23 | 24 | 25 |

Work with your group to summarize the data sets with numbers and box plots.

1. Write the five-number summary for the data for each airplane. Then, calculate the interquartile range for each data set.

min	Q1	median	Q3	max	IQR

2. Draw three box plots, one for each paper airplane. Label the box plots clearly.

distance in yards

3. How are the results for Andre and Lin's planes the same? How are they different?

4. How are the results for Lin and Noah's planes the same? How are they different?

Are you ready for more?

Priya joined in the paper-plane experiments. She launched her plane eleven times and recorded the lengths of each flight. She found that her maximum and minimum were equal to Lin's. Her IQR was equal to Andre's.

Draw a box plot that could represent Priya's data.

distance in yards

With the information given, can you estimate the median for Priya's data? Explain your reasoning.

iV KH

Lesson 17 Summary

Box plots are useful for comparing different groups. Here are two sets of plots that show the weights of some berries and some grapes.

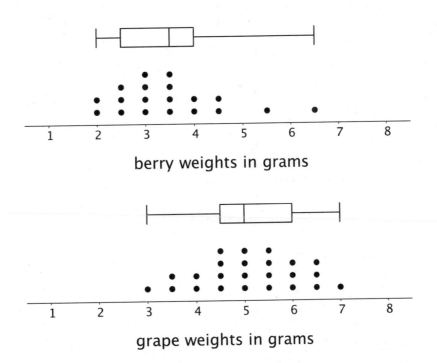

berry weights in grams

grape weights in grams

Notice that the median berry weight is 3.5 grams and the median grape weight is 5 grams. In both cases, the IQR is 1.5 grams. Because the grapes in this group have a higher median weight than the berries, we can say a grape in the group is typically heavier than a berry. Because both groups have the same IQR, we can say that they have a similar variability in their weights.

These box plots represent the length data for a collection of ladybugs and a collection of beetles.

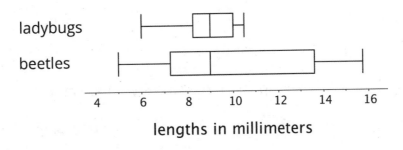

lengths in millimeters

The medians of the two collections are the same, but the IQR of the ladybugs is much smaller. This tells us that a typical ladybug length is similar to a typical beetle length, but the ladybugs are more alike in their length than the beetles are in their length.

Lesson 17 Practice Problems

1. Here are box plots that summarize the heights of 20 professional male athletes in basketball, football, hockey, and baseball.

height in inches

   a. In which two sports are the players' height distributions most alike? Explain your reasoning.

   b. Which sport shows the greatest variability in players' heights? Which sport shows the least variability?

2. Here is a box plot that summarizes data for the time, in minutes, that a fire department took to respond to 100 emergency calls.

   Select **all** the statements that are true, according to the dot plot.

   time in minutes

   A. Most of the response times were under 13 minutes.

   B. Fewer than 30 of the response times were over 13 minutes.

   C. More than half of the response times were 11 minutes or greater.

   D. There were more response times that were greater than 13 minutes than those that were less than 9 minutes.

   E. About 75% of the response times were 13 minutes or less.

iM KH

3. Pineapples were packed in three large crates. For each crate, the weight of every pineapple in the crate was recorded. Here are three box plots that summarize the weights in each crate.

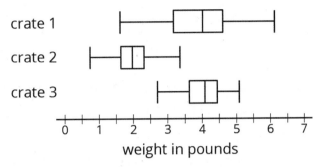

Select **all** of the statements that are true, according to the box plots.

A. The weights of the pineapples in Crate 1 were the most variable.

B. The heaviest pineapple was in Crate 1.

C. The lightest pineapple was in Crate 1.

D. Crate 3 had the greatest median weight and the greatest IQR.

E. More than half the pineapples in Crate 1 and Crate 3 were heavier than the heaviest pineapple in Crate 2.

4. Two TV shows each asked 100 viewers for their ages. For one show, the mean age of the viewers was 35 years and the MAD was 20 years. For the other show, the mean age of the viewers was 30 years and the MAD was 5 years.

A sixth-grade student says he watches one of the shows. Which show do you think he watches? Explain your reasoning.

(From Unit 8, Lesson 12.)

Lesson 18: Using Data to Solve Problems

Let's compare data sets using visual displays.

18.1: Wild Bears

In one study on wild bears, researchers measured the head lengths and head widths, in inches, of 143 wild bears. The ages of the bears ranged from newborns (0 years) to 15 years. The box plots summarize the data from the study.

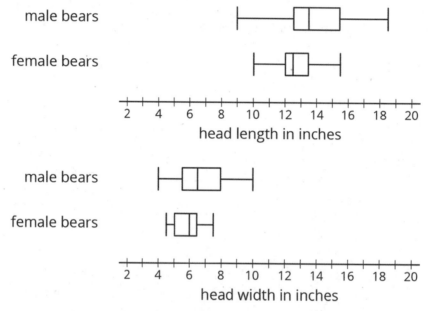

1. Write four statistical questions that could be answered using the box plots: two questions about the head length and two questions about the head width.

2. Trade questions with your partner.

   a. Decide if each question is a statistical question.

   b. Use the box plots to answer each question.

iM KH

18.2: Math Homework (Part 1)

Over a two-week period, Mai recorded the number of math homework problems she had each school day.

2 15 20 0 5 25 1 0 10 12

1. Calculate the following. Show your reasoning.

    a. The mean number of math homework problems

    b. The mean absolute deviation (MAD)

2. Interpret the mean and MAD. What do they tell you about the number of homework problems Mai had over these two weeks?

3. Find or calculate the following values and show your reasoning.

    a. The median, quartiles, maximum, and minimum of Mai's data

    b. The interquartile range (IQR)

4. Which pair of measures of center and variability—mean and MAD, or median and IQR—do you think summarizes the distribution of Mai's math homework assignments better? Explain your reasoning.

18.3: Math Homework (Part 2)

Jada wanted to know whether a dot plot, a histogram, or a box plot would best summarize the center, variability, and other aspects of her homework data.

| 2 | 15 | 20 | 0 | 5 | 25 | 1 | 0 | 10 | 12 |

1. Use the axis to make a dot plot to represent the data. Mark the position of the mean, which you calculated earlier, on the dot plot using a triangle (Δ). From the triangle, draw a horizontal line segment to the left and right sides to represent the MAD.

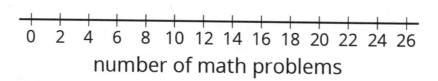

number of math problems

2. Draw a box plot that represents Jada's homework data.

number of math problems

3. Work with your group to draw three histograms to represent Jada's homework data. The width of the bars in each histogram should represent a different number of homework problems, which are specified as follows.

iM KH

a. The width of one bar represents 10 problems.

number of math problems

b. The width of one bar represents 5 problems.

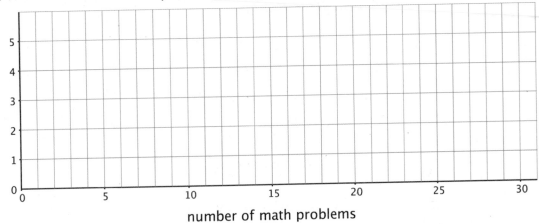

number of math problems

c. The width of one bar represents 2 problems.

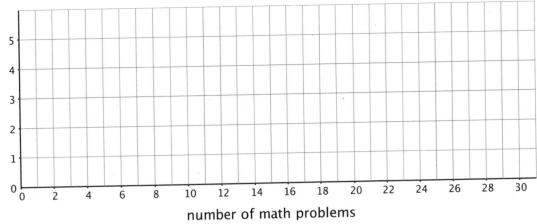

number of math problems

4. Which of the five representations should Jada use to summarize her data? Should she use a dot plot, box plot, or one of the histograms? Explain your reasoning.

18.4: Will the Yellow Perch Survive?

Scientists studying the yellow perch, a species of fish, believe that the length of a fish is related to its age. This means that the longer the fish, the older it is. Adult yellow perch vary in size, but they are usually between 10 and 25 centimeters.

Scientists at the Great Lakes Water Institute caught, measured, and released yellow perch at several locations in Lake Michigan. The following summary is based on a sample of yellow perch from one of these locations.

length of fish in centimeters	number of fish
0 to less than 5	5
5 to less than 10	7
10 to less than 15	14
15 to less than 20	20
20 to less than 25	24
25 to less than 30	30

1. Use the data to make a histogram that shows the lengths of the captured yellow perch. Each bar should contain the lengths shown in each row in the table.

fish length in centimeters

iM KH

2. How many fish were measured? How do you know?

3. Use the histogram to answer the following questions.

   a. How would you describe the shape of the distribution?

   b. Estimate the median length for this sample. Describe how you made this estimate.

   c. Predict whether the mean length of this sample is greater than, less than, or nearly equal to the median length for this sample of fish? Explain your prediction.

   d. Would you use the mean or the median to describe a typical length of the fish being studied? Explain your reasoning.

4. Based on your work so far:

   a. Would you describe a typical age for the yellow perch in this sample as: "young," "adult," or "old"? Explain your reasoning.

   b. Some researchers are concerned about the survival of the yellow perch. Do you think the lengths (or the ages) of the fish in this sample are something to worry about? Explain your reasoning.

Lesson 18 Summary

The dot plot shows the distribution of 30 cookie weights in grams.

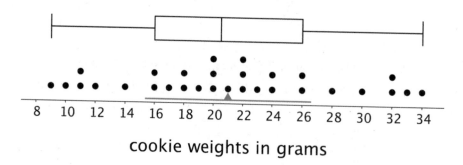

cookie weights in grams

The mean cookie weight, marked by the triangle, is 21 grams. This tells us that if the weights of all of the cookies were redistributed so they all had the same weight, each cookie would weigh 21 grams. The MAD is 5.6 grams, which suggests that a cookie typically weighs between 15.4 grams and 26.6 grams.

The box plot for the same data set is shown above the dot plot. The median shows that half of the weights are greater than or equal to 20.5 grams, and half are less than or equal to 20.5 grams. The box shows that the IQR is 10 and that the middle half of the cookies weigh between 16 and 26 grams.

In this case, the median weight is very close to the mean weight, and the IQR is about twice the MAD. This tells us that the two pairs of measures of center and spread are very similar.

iM KH

Now let's look at another example of 30 different cookies.

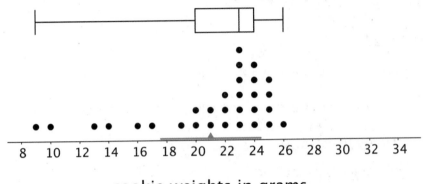

cookie weights in grams

Here the mean is 21 grams, and the MAD is 3.4 grams. This suggests that a cookie typically weighs between 17.6 and 24.4 grams. The median cookie weight is 23 grams, and the box plot shows that the middle half of the data are between 20 and 24 grams. These two pairs of measures paint very different pictures of the variability of the cookie weights.

The median (23 grams) is closer to the middle of the big cluster of values. If we were to ignore the smaller cookies, the median and IQR would give a more accurate picture of how much a cookie typically weighs.

When a distribution is not symmetrical, the median and IQR are often better measures of center and spread than the mean and MAD. However the decision on which pair of measures to use depends on what we want to know about the group we are investigating.

Learning Targets

Lesson 1: Got Data?

- I can collect the correct data to answer a question and use the correct units.

- I can explain the difference between categorical and numerical data.

Lesson 2: Statistical Questions

- I can tell when data has variability.

Lesson 3: Representing Data Graphically

- I can describe the information presented in tables, dot plots, and bar graphs.

- I can use tables, dot plots, and bar graphs to represent distributions of data.

Lesson 4: Dot Plots

- I can describe the center and spread of data from a dot plot.

Lesson 5: Using Dot Plots to Answer Statistical Questions

- I can use a dot plot to represent the distribution of a data set and answer questions about the real-world situation.

- I can use center and spread to describe data sets, including what is typical in a data set.

Lesson 6: Interpreting Histograms

- I can recognize when a histogram is an appropriate graphical display of a data set.

- I can use a histogram to get information about the distribution of data and explain what it means in a real-world situation.

Lesson 7: Using Histograms to Answer Statistical Questions

- I can draw a histogram from a table of data.

- I can use a histogram to describe the distribution of data and determine a typical value for the data.

iM KH

Lesson 8: Describing Distributions on Histograms

- I can describe the shape and features of a histogram and explain what they mean in the context of the data.

- I can distinguish histograms and bar graphs.

Lesson 9: Mean

- I can explain how the mean for a data set represents a "fair share."

- I can find the mean for a numerical data set.

Lesson 10: Finding and Interpreting the Mean as the Balance Point

- I can describe what the mean tells us in the context of the data.

- I can explain how the mean represents a balance point for the data on a dot plot.

Lesson 11: Variability and MAD

- I can find the MAD for a set of data.

- I know what the mean absolute deviation (MAD) measures and what information it provides.

Lesson 12: Using Mean and MAD to Make Comparisons

- I can say what the MAD tells us in a given context.

- I can use means and MADs to compare groups.

Lesson 13: Median

- I can find the median for a set of data.

- I can say what the median represents and what it tells us in a given context.

Lesson 14: Comparing Mean and Median

- I can determine when the mean or the median is more appropriate to describe the center of data.

- I can explain how the distribution of data affects the mean and the median.

Lesson 15: Quartiles and Interquartile Range

- I can use IQR to describe the spread of data.

- I know what quartiles and interquartile range (IQR) measure and what they tell us about the data.

- When given a list of data values or a dot plot, I can find the quartiles and interquartile range (IQR) for data.

Lesson 16: Box Plots

- I can use the five-number summary to draw a box plot.

- I know what information a box plot shows and how it is constructed.

Lesson 17: Using Box Plots

- I can use a box plot to answer questions about a data set.

- I can use medians and IQRs to compare groups.

Lesson 18: Using Data to Solve Problems

- I can decide whether mean and MAD or median and IQR would be more appropriate for describing the center and spread of a data set.

- I can draw an appropriate graphical representation for a set of data.

- I can explain what the mean and MAD or the median and IQR tell us in the context of a situation and use them to answer questions.

iM KH

GRADE 6

Unit

9

STUDENT EDITION
Book 3

Kendall Hunt |

Lesson 1: Fermi Problems

Let's make some estimates.

1.1: Ant Trek

How long would it take an ant to run from Los Angeles to New York City?

1.2: Stacks and Stacks of Cereal Boxes

Imagine a warehouse that has a rectangular floor and that contains all of the boxes of breakfast cereal bought in the United States in one year.

If the warehouse is 10 feet tall, what could the side lengths of the floor be?

iM KH

1.3: Covering the Washington Monument

How many tiles would it take to cover the
Washington Monument?

Lesson 2: If Our Class Were the World

Let's use math to better understand our world.

2.1: All 7.4 Billion of Us

There are 7.4 billion people in the world. If the whole world were represented by a 30-person class:

- 14 people would eat rice as their main food.
- 12 people would be under the age of 20.
- 5 people would be from Africa.

1. How many people in the class would *not* eat rice as their main food?

2. What percentage of the people in the class would be under the age of 20?

3. Based on the number of people in the class representing people from Africa, how many people live in Africa?

2.2: About the People in the World

With the members of your group, write a list of questions about the people in the world. Your questions should begin with "How many people in the world. . ." Then, choose several questions on the list that you find most interesting.

2.3: If Our Class Were the World

Suppose your class represents all the people in the world.

Choose several characteristics about the world's population that you have investigated. Find the number of students in *your* class that would have the same characteristics.

Create a visual display that includes a diagram that represents this information. Give your display the title "If Our Class Were the World."

Lesson 3: Rectangle Madness

Let's cut up rectangles.

3.1: Squares in Rectangles

1. Rectangle $ABCD$ is not a square. Rectangle $ABEF$ is a square.

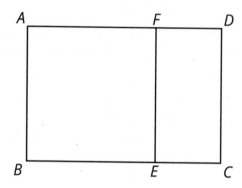

a. Suppose segment AF were 5 units long and segment FD were 2 units long. How long would segment AD be?

b. Suppose segment BC were 10 units long and segment BE were 6 units long. How long would segment EC be?

c. Suppose segment AF were 12 units long and segment FD were 5 units long. How long would segment FE be?

d. Suppose segment AD were 9 units long and segment AB were 5 units long. How long would segment FD be?

iM KH

2. Rectangle $JKXW$ has been decomposed into squares.

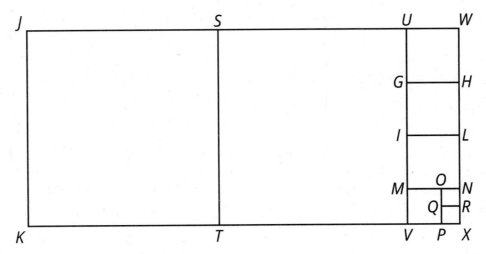

Segment JK is 33 units long and segment JW is 75 units long. Find the areas of all of the squares in the diagram.

3. Rectangle $ABCD$ is 16 units by 5 units.

a. In the diagram, draw a line segment that decomposes $ABCD$ into two regions: a square that is the largest possible and a new rectangle.

b. Draw another line segment that decomposes the *new* rectangle into two regions: a square that is the largest possible and another new rectangle.

c. Keep going until rectangle $ABCD$ is entirely decomposed into squares.

d. List the side lengths of all the squares in your diagram.

1. The diagram shows that rectangle $VWYZ$ has been decomposed into three squares. What could the side lengths of this rectangle be?

2. How many different side lengths can you find for rectangle $VWYZ$?

3. What are some rules for possible side lengths of rectangle $VWYZ$?

3.2: More Rectangles, More Squares

1. Draw a rectangle that is 21 units by 6 units.

   a. In your rectangle, draw a line segment that decomposes the rectangle into a new rectangle and a square that is as large as possible. Continue until the diagram shows that your original rectangle has been entirely decomposed into squares.

   b. How many squares of each size are in your diagram?

   c. What is the side length of the smallest square?

2. Draw a rectangle that is 28 units by 12 units.

   a. In your rectangle, draw a line segment that decomposes the rectangle into a new rectangle and a square that is as large as possible. Continue until the diagram shows that your original rectangle has been decomposed into squares.

   b. How many squares of each size are in your diagram?

   c. What is the side length of the smallest square?

3. Write each of these fractions as a mixed number with the smallest possible numerator and denominator:

   a. $\frac{16}{5}$

   b. $\frac{21}{6}$

   c. $\frac{28}{12}$

4. What do the fraction problems have to do with the previous rectangle decomposition problems?

3.3: Finding Equivalent Fractions

1. Accurately draw a rectangle that is 9 units by 4 units.

   a. In your rectangle, draw a line segment that decomposes the rectangle into a new rectangle and a square that is as large as possible. Continue until your original rectangle has been entirely decomposed into squares.

   b. How many squares of each size are there?

   c. What are the side lengths of the last square you drew?

   d. Write $\frac{9}{4}$ as a mixed number.

iM KH

2. Accurately draw a rectangle that is 27 units by 12 units.

    a. In your rectangle, draw a line segment that decomposes the rectangle into a new rectangle and a square that is as large as possible. Continue until your original rectangle has been entirely decomposed into squares.

    b. How many squares of each size are there?

    c. What are the side lengths of the last square you drew?

    d. Write $\frac{27}{12}$ as a mixed number.

    e. Compare the diagram you drew for this problem and the one for the previous problem. How are they the same? How are they different?

3. What is the greatest common factor of 9 and 4? What is the greatest common factor of 27 and 12? What does this have to do with your diagrams of decomposed rectangles?

Are you ready for more?

We have seen some examples of rectangle tilings. A *tiling* means a way to completely cover a shape with other shapes, without any gaps or overlaps. For example, here is a tiling of rectangle $KXWJ$ with 2 large squares, 3 medium squares, 1 small square, and 2 tiny squares.

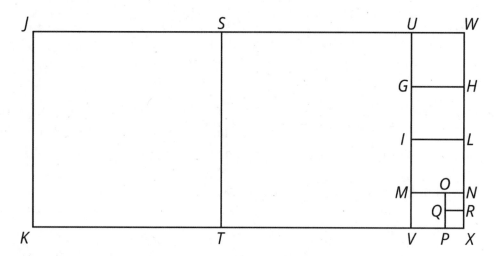

Some of the squares used to tile this rectangle have the same size.

Might it be possible to tile a rectangle with squares where the squares are *all different sizes*?

If you think it is possible, find such a rectangle and such a tiling. If you think it is not possible, explain why it is not possible.

3.4: It's All About Fractions

1. Accurately draw a 37-by-16 rectangle. (Use graph paper, if possible.)

   a. In your rectangle, draw a line segment that decomposes the rectangle into a new rectangle and a square that is as large as possible. Continue until your original rectangle has been entirely decomposed into squares.

   b. How many squares of each size are there?

   c. What are the dimensions of the last square you drew?

   d. What does this have to do with $2 + \dfrac{1}{3+\frac{1}{5}}$?

2. Consider a 52-by-15 rectangle.

    a. In your rectangle, draw a line segment that decomposes the rectangle into a new rectangle and a square that is as large as possible. Continue until your original rectangle has been entirely decomposed into squares.

    b. Write a fraction equal to this expression: $3 + \dfrac{1}{2 + \frac{1}{7}}$.

    c. Notice some connections between the rectangle and the fraction.

    d. What is the greatest common factor of 52 and 15?

3. Consider a 98-by-21 rectangle.

a. In your rectangle, draw a line segment that decomposes the rectangle into a new rectangle and a square that is as large as possible. Continue until your original rectangle has been entirely decomposed into squares.

b. Write a fraction equal to this expression: $4 + \dfrac{1}{1 + \dfrac{7}{14}}$.

c. Notice some connections between the rectangle and the fraction.

d. What is the greatest common factor of 98 and 21?

4. Consider a 121-by-38 rectangle.

    a. Use the decomposition-into-squares process to write a continued fraction for $\frac{121}{38}$. Verify that it works.

    b. What is the greatest common factor of 121 and 38?

iM KH

Lesson 4: How Do We Choose?

Let's vote and choose a winner!

4.1: Which Was "Yessier"?

Two sixth-grade classes, A and B, voted on whether to give the answers to their math problems in poetry. The "yes" choice was more popular in both classes.

	yes	no
class A	24	16
class B	18	9

Was one class more in favor of math poetry, or were they equally in favor? Find three or more ways to answer the question.

4.2: Which Class Voted Purpler?

The school will be painted over the summer. Students get to vote on whether to change the color to purple (a "yes" vote), or keep it a beige color (a "no" vote).

The principal of the school decided to analyze voting results by class. The table shows some results.

In both classes, a majority voted for changing the paint color to purple. Which class was more in favor of changing?

	yes	no
class A	26	14
class B	31	19

4.3: Supermajorities

1. Another school is also voting on whether to change their school's color to purple. Their rules require a $\frac{2}{3}$ supermajority to change the colors. A total of 240 people voted, and 153 voted to change to purple. Were there enough votes to make the change?

2. This school also is thinking of changing their mascot to an armadillo. To change mascots, a 55% supermajority is needed. How many of the 240 students need to vote "yes" for the mascot to change?

3. At this school, which requires more votes to pass: a change of mascot or a change of color?

4.4: Best Restaurant

A town's newspaper held a contest to decide the best restaurant in town. Only people who subscribe to the newspaper can vote. 25% of the people in town subscribe to the newspaper. 20% of the subscribers voted. 80% of the people who voted liked Darnell's BBQ Pit best.

Darnell put a big sign in his restaurant's window that said, "80% say Darnell's is the best!"

Do you think Darnell's sign is making an accurate statement? Support your answer with:

- Some calculations
- An explanation in words
- A diagram that accurately represents the people in town, the newspaper subscribers, the voters, and the people who liked Darnell's best

Lesson 5: More than Two Choices

Let's explore different ways to determine a winner.

5.1: Field Day

Students in a sixth-grade class were asked, "What activity would you most like to do for field day?" The results are shown in the table.

activity	number of votes
softball game	16
scavenger hunt	10
dancing talent show	8
marshmallow throw	4
no preference	2

1. What percentage of the class voted for softball?

2. What percentage did not vote for softball as their first choice?

iM KH

5.2: School Lunches (Part 1)

Suppose students at our school are voting for the lunch menu over the course of one week. The following is a list of options provided by the caterer.

Menu 1: Meat Lovers

- Meat loaf
- Hot dogs
- Pork cutlets
- Beef stew
- Liver and onions

Menu 2: Vegetarian

- Vegetable soup and peanut butter sandwich
- Hummus, pita, and veggie sticks
- Veggie burgers and fries
- Chef's salad
- Cheese pizza every day
- Double desserts every day

Menu 3: Something for Everyone

- Chicken nuggets
- Burgers and fries
- Pizza
- Tacos
- Leftover day (all the week's leftovers made into a casserole)
- Bonus side dish: pea jello (green gelatin with canned peas)

Menu 4: Concession Stand

- Choice of hamburger or hot dog, with fries, every day

To vote, draw one of the following symbols next to each menu option to show your first, second, third, and last choices. If you use the slips of paper from your teacher, use only the column that says "symbol."

1st choice   2nd choice   3rd choice   4th choice

1. Meat Lovers _____

2. Vegetarian _____

3. Something for Everyone _____

4. Concession Stand _____

Here are two voting systems that can be used to determine the winner.

- Voting System #1. *Plurality*: The option with the most first-choice votes (stars) wins.

- Voting System #2. *Runoff*: If no choice received a majority of the votes, leave out the choice that received the fewest first-choice votes (stars). Then have another vote.

If your first vote is still a choice, vote for that. If not, vote for your second choice that you wrote down.

If there is still no majority, leave out the choice that got the fewest votes, and then vote again. Vote for your first choice if it's still in, and if not, vote for your second choice. If your second choice is also out, vote for your third choice.

1. How many people in our class are voting? How many votes does it take to win a majority?

2. How many votes did the top option receive? Was this a majority of the votes?

3. People tend to be more satisfied with election results if their top choices win. For how many, and what percentage, of people was the winning option:

   a. their first choice?

   b. their second choice?

   c. their third choice?

   d. their last choice?

4. After the second round of voting, did any choice get a majority? If so, is it the same choice that got a plurality in Voting System #1?

5. Which choice won?

6. How satisfied were the voters by the election results? For how many, and what percentage, of people was the winning option:

   a. their first choice?

   b. their second choice?

   c. their third choice?

   d. their last choice?

7. Compare the satisfaction results for the plurality voting rule and the runoff rule. Did one produce satisfactory results for more people than the other?

5.3: School Lunch (Part 2)

Let's analyze a different election.

In another class, there are four clubs. Everyone in each club agrees to vote for the lunch menu exactly the same way, as shown in this table.

	Barbecue Club (21 members)	Garden Club (13 members)	Sports Boosters (7 members)	Film Club (9 members)
A. Meat Lovers	☆ (star)	✕	✕	✕
B. Vegetarian	☺	☆ (star)	😐 (neutral square)	😐 (neutral square)
C. Something for Everyone	😐 (neutral square)	😐 (neutral square)	☺	☆ (star)
D. Concession Stand	✕	☺	☆ (star)	☺

1. Figure out which option won the election by answering these questions.

    a. On the first vote, when everyone voted for their first choice, how many votes did each option get? Did any choice get a majority?

    b. Which option is removed from the next vote?

    c. On the second vote, how many votes did each of the remaining three menu options get? Did any option get a majority?

    d. Which menu option is removed from the next vote?

    e. On the third vote, how many votes did each of the remaining two options get? Which option won?

iM KH

2. Estimate how satisfied all the voters were.

    a. For how many people was the winner their first choice?

    b. For how many people was the winner their second choice?

    c. For how many people was the winner their third choice?

    d. For how many people was the winner their last choice?

3. Compare the satisfaction results for the plurality voting rule and the runoff rule. Did one produce satisfactory results for more people than the other?

5.4: Just Vote Once

Your class just voted using the *instant runoff* system. Use the class data for following questions.

1. For our class, which choice received the most points?

2. Does this result agree with that from the runoff election in an earlier activity?

3. For the other class, which choice received the most points?

4. Does this result agree with that from the runoff election in an earlier activity?

5. The runoff method uses information about people's first, second, third, and last choices when it is not clear that there is a winner from everyone's first choices. How does the instant runoff method include the same information?

6. After comparing the results for the three voting rules (plurality, runoff, instant runoff) and the satisfaction surveys, which method do you think is fairest? Explain.

Are you ready for more?

Numbering your choices 0 through 3 might not really describe your opinions. For example, what if you really liked A and C a lot, and you really hated B and D? You might want to give A and C both a 3, and B and D both a 0.

1. Design a numbering system where the size of the number accurately shows how much you like a choice. Some ideas:

   ○ The same 0 to 3 scale, but you can choose more than one of each number, or even decimals between 0 and 3.
   ○ A scale of 1 to 10, with 10 for the best and 1 for the worst.

2. Try out your system with the people in your group, using the same school lunch options for the election.

3. Do you think your system gives a more fair way to make choices? Explain your reasoning.

iM KH

5.5: Weekend Choices

Clare, Han, Mai, Tyler, and Noah are deciding what to do on the weekend. Their options are cooking, hiking, and bowling. Here are the points for their instant runoff vote. Each first choice gets 2 points, the second choice gets 1 point, and the last choice gets 0 points.

	cooking	hiking	bowling
Clare	2	1	0
Han	2	1	0
Mai	2	1	0
Tyler	0	2	1
Noah	0	2	1

1. Which activity won using the instant runoff method? Show your calculations and use expressions or equations.

2. Which activity would have won if there was just a vote for their top choice, with a majority or plurality winning?

3. Which activity would have won if there was a runoff election?

4. Explain why this happened.

Lesson 6: Picking Representatives

Let's think about fair representation.

6.1: Computers for Kids

A program gives computers to families with school-aged children. They have a certain number of computers to distribute fairly between several families. How many computers should each family get?

1. One month the program has 8 computers. The families have these numbers of school-aged children: 4, 2, 6, 2, 2.

   a. How many children are there in all?

   b. Counting all the children in all the families, how many children would use each computer? This is the number of children per computer. Call this number A.

   c. Fill in the third column of the table. Decide how many computers to give to each family if we use A as the basis for distributing the computers.

family	number of children	number of computers, using A
Baum	4	
Chu	2	
Davila	6	
Eno	2	
Farouz	2	

   d. Check that 8 computers have been given out in all.

2. The next month they again have 8 computers. There are different families with these numbers of children: 3, 1, 2, 5, 1, 8.

    a. How many children are there in all?

    b. Counting all the children in all the families, how many children would use each computer? This is the number of children per computer. Call this number B.

    c. Does it make sense that B is not a whole number? Why?

    d. Fill in the third column of the table. Decide how many computers to give to each family if we use B as the basis for distributing the computers.

family	number of children	number of computers, using B	number of computers, your way	children per computer, your way
Gray	3			
Hernandez	1			
Ito	2			
Jones	5			
Krantz	1			
Lo	8			

    e. Check that 8 computers have been given out in all.

    f. Does it make sense that the number of computers for one family is not a whole number? Explain your reasoning.

    g. Find and describe a way to distribute computers to the families so that each family gets a whole number of computers. Fill in the fourth column of the table.

h. Compute the number of children per computer in each family and fill in the last column of the table.

i. Do you think your way of distributing the computers is fair? Explain your reasoning.

6.2: School Mascot (Part 1)

A school is deciding on a school mascot. They have narrowed the choices down to the Banana Slugs or the Sea Lions.

The principal decided that each class gets one vote. Each class held an election, and the winning choice was the one vote for the whole class. The table shows how three classes voted.

	banana slugs	sea lions	class vote
class A	9	3	banana slug
class B	14	10	
class C	6	30	

1. Which mascot won, according to the principal's plan? What percentage of the votes did the winner get under this plan?

2. Which mascot received the most student votes in all? What percentage of the votes did this mascot receive?

3. The students thought this plan was not very fair. They suggested that bigger classes should have more votes to send to the principal. Make up a proposal for the principal where there are as few votes as possible, but the votes proportionally represent the number of students in each class.

4. Decide how to assign the votes for the results in the class. (Do they all go to the winner? Or should the loser still get some votes?)

5. In your system, which mascot is the winner?

6. In your system, how many representative votes are there? How many students does each vote represent?

6.3: Advising the School Board

1. In a very small school district, there are four schools, D, E, F, and G. The district wants a total of 10 advisors for the students. Each school should have at least one advisor.

school	number of students	number of advisors, using A
D	48	
E	12	
F	24	
G	36	

a. How many students are in this district in all?

b. If the advisors could represent students at different schools, how many students per advisor should there be? Call this number A.

c. Using A students per advisor, how many advisors should each school have? Complete the table with this information for schools D, E, F, and G.

2. Another district has four schools; some are large, others are small. The district wants 10 advisors in all. Each school should have at least one advisor.

school	number of students	number of advisors, using B	number of advisors, your way	students per advisor, your way
Dr. King School	500			
O'Connor School	200			
Science Magnet School	140			
Trombone Academy	10			

a. How many students are in this district in all?

b. If the advisors didn't have to represent students at the same school, how many students per advisor should there be? Call this number B.

c. Using B students per advisor, how many advisors should each school have? Give your quotients to the tenths place. Fill in the first "number of advisors" column of the table. Does it make sense to have a tenth of an advisor?

d. Decide on a consistent way to assign advisors to schools so that there are only whole numbers of advisors for each school, and there is a total of 10 advisors among the schools. Fill in the "your way" column of the table.

e. How many students per advisor are there at each school? Fill in the last row of the table.

f. Do you think this is a fair way to assign advisors? Explain your reasoning.

iM KH

6.4: School Mascot (Part 2)

The whole town gets interested in choosing a mascot. The mayor of the town decides to choose representatives to vote.

There are 50 blocks in the town, and the people on each block tend to have the same opinion about which mascot is best. Green blocks like sea lions, and gold blocks like banana slugs. The mayor decides to have 5 representatives, each representing a district of 10 blocks.

Here is a map of the town, with preferences shown.

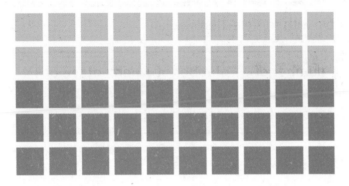

1. Suppose there were an election with each block getting one vote. How many votes would be for banana slugs? For sea lions? What percentage of the vote would be for banana slugs?

2. Suppose the districts are shown in the next map. What did the people in each district prefer? What did their representative vote? Which mascot would win the election?

Complete the table with this election's results.

district	number of blocks for banana slugs	number of blocks for sea lions	percentage of blocks for banana slugs	representative's vote
1	10	0		banana slugs
2				
3				
4				
5				

iM KH

3. Suppose, instead, that the districts are shown in the new map below. What did the people in each district prefer? What did their representative vote? Which mascot would win the election?

Complete the table with this election's results.

district	number of blocks for banana slugs	number of blocks for sea lions	percentage of blocks for banana slugs	representative's vote
1				
2				
3				
4				
5				

4. Suppose the districts are designed in yet another way, as shown in the next map. What did the people in each district prefer? What did their representative vote? Which mascot would win the election?

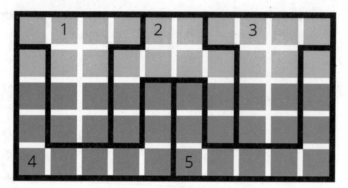

Complete the table with this election's results.

district	number of blocks for banana slugs	number of blocks for sea lions	percentage of blocks for banana slugs	representative's vote
1				
2				
3				
4				
5				

5. Write a headline for the local newspaper for each of the ways of splitting the town into districts.

6. Which systems on the three maps of districts do you think are more fair? Are any totally unfair?

iM KH

6.5: Fair and Unfair Districts

1. Smallville's map is shown, with opinions shown by block in green and gold. Decompose the map to create three connected, equal-area districts in two ways:

a. Design three districts where *green* will win at least two of the three districts. Record results in Table 1.

Table 1:

district	number of blocks for green	number of blocks for gold	percentage of blocks for green	representative's vote
1				
2				
3				

b. Design three districts where *gold* will win at least two of the three districts. Record results in Table 2.

Table 2:

district	number of blocks for green	number of blocks for gold	percentage of blocks for green	representative's vote
1				
2				
3				

2. Squaretown's map is shown, with opinions by block shown in green and gold. Decompose the map to create five connected, equal-area districts in two ways:

a. Design five districts where *green* will win at least three of the five districts. Record the results in Table 3.

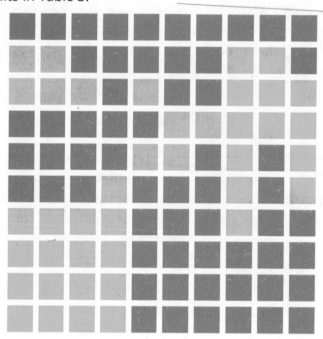

Table 3:

district	number of blocks for green	number of blocks for gold	percentage of blocks for green	representative's vote
1				
2				
3				
4				
5				

iM KH

b. Design five districts where *gold* will win at least three of the five districts. Record the results in Table 4.

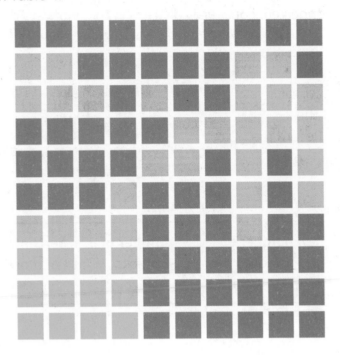

Table 4:

district	number of blocks for green	number of blocks for gold	percentage of blocks for green	representative's vote
1				
2				
3				
4				
5				

3. Mountain Valley's map is shown, with opinions by block shown in green and gold. (This is a town in a narrow valley in the mountains.) Can you decompose the map to create three connected, equal-area districts in the two ways described here?

a. Design three districts where *green* will win at least 2 of the 3 districts. Record the results in Table 5.

Table 5:

district	number of blocks for green	number of blocks for gold	percentage of blocks for green	representative's vote
1				
2				
3				

b. Design three districts where *gold* will win at least 2 of the 3 districts. Record the results in Table 6.

Table 6:

district	number of blocks for green	number of blocks for gold	percentage of blocks for green	representative's vote
1				
2				
3				

iM KH

Glossary

absolute value

The absolute value of a number is its distance from 0 on the number line.

The absolute value of -7 is 7, because it is 7 units away from 0. The absolute value of 5 is 5, because it is 5 units away from 0.

area

Area is the number of square units that cover a two-dimensional region, without any gaps or overlaps.

For example, the area of region A is 8 square units. The area of the shaded region of B is $\frac{1}{2}$ square unit.

A   B

average

The average is another name for the mean of a data set.

For the data set 3, 5, 6, 8, 11, 12, the average is 7.5.

$$3 + 5 + 6 + 8 + 11 + 12 = 45$$

$$45 \div 6 = 7.5$$

base (of a parallelogram or triangle)

We can choose any side of a parallelogram or triangle to be the shape's base. Sometimes we use the word *base* to refer to the length of this side.

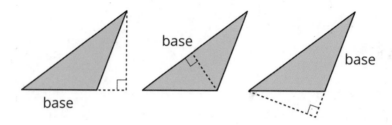

base (of a prism or pyramid)

The word *base* can also refer to a face of a polyhedron.

A prism has two identical bases that are parallel. A pyramid has one base.

A prism or pyramid is named for the shape of its base.

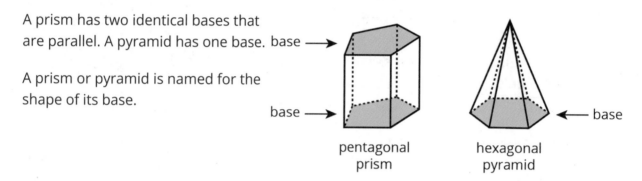

pentagonal prism

hexagonal pyramid

box plot

A box plot is a way to represent data on a number line. The data is divided into four sections. The sides of the box represent the first and third quartiles. A line inside the box represents the median. Lines outside the box connect to the minimum and maximum values.

For example, this box plot shows a data set with a minimum of 2 and a maximum of 15. The median is 6, the first quartile is 5, and the third quartile is 10.

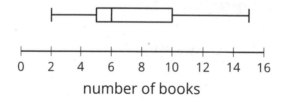

number of books

categorical data

A set of categorical data has values that are words instead of numbers.

For example, Han asks 5 friends to name their favorite color. Their answers are: blue, blue, green, blue, orange.

center

The center of a set of numerical data is a value in the middle of the distribution. It represents a typical value for the data set.

For example, the center of this distribution of cat weights is between 4.5 and 5 kilograms.

cat weights in kilograms

coefficient
A coefficient is a number that is multiplied by a variable.

For example, in the expression $3x + 5$, the coefficient of x is 3. In the expression $y + 5$, the coefficient of y is 1, because $y = 1 \cdot y$.

common factor
A common factor of two numbers is a number that divides evenly into both numbers. For example, 5 is a common factor of 15 and 20, because $15 \div 5 = 3$ and $20 \div 5 = 4$. Both of the quotients, 3 and 4, are whole numbers.

- The factors of 15 are 1, 3, *5*, and 15.

- The factors of 20 are 1, 2, 4, *5*, 10, and 20.

common multiple
A common multiple of two numbers is a product you can get by multiplying each of the two numbers by some whole number. For example, 30 is a common multiple of 3 and 5, because $3 \cdot 10 = 30$ and $5 \cdot 6 = 30$. Both of the factors, 10 and 6, are whole numbers.

- The multiples of 3 are 3, 6, 9, 12, *15*, 18, 21, 24, 27, *30*, 33 . . .

- The multiples of 5 are 5, 10, *15*, 20, 25, *30*, 35, 40 . . .

The common multiples of 3 and 5 are 15, 30, 45, 60 . . .

compose
Compose means "put together." We use the word *compose* to describe putting more than one figure together to make a new shape.

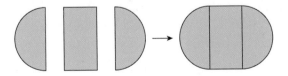

coordinate plane

The coordinate plane is a system for telling where points are. For example. point R is located at $(3, 2)$ on the coordinate plane, because it is three units to the right and two units up.

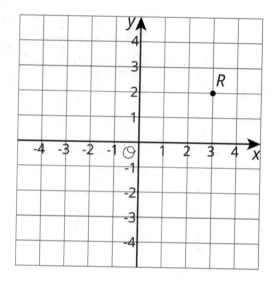

cubed

We use the word *cubed* to mean "to the third power." This is because a cube with side length s has a volume of $s \cdot s \cdot s$, or s^3.

decompose

Decompose means "take apart." We use the word *decompose* to describe taking a figure apart to make more than one new shape.

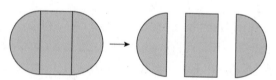

iM KH

dependent variable

The dependent variable is the result of a calculation.

For example, a boat travels at a constant speed of 25 miles per hour. The equation $d = 25t$ describes the relationship between the boat's distance and time. The dependent variable is the distance traveled, because d is the result of multiplying 25 by t.

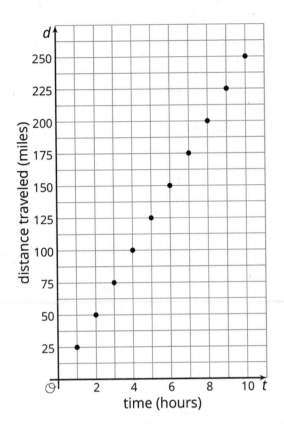

distribution

The distribution tells how many times each value occurs in a data set. For example, in the data set blue, blue, green, blue, orange, the distribution is 3 blues, 1 green, and 1 orange.

Here is a dot plot that shows the distribution for the data set 6, 10, 7, 35, 7, 36, 32, 10, 7, 35.

dot plot

A dot plot is a way to represent data on a number line. Each time a value appears in the data set, we put another dot above that number on the number line.

For example, in this dot plot there are three dots above the 9. This means that three different plants had a height of 9 cm.

plant height (centimeters)

double number line diagram

A double number line diagram uses a pair of parallel number lines to represent equivalent ratios. The locations of the tick marks match on both number lines. The tick marks labeled 0 line up, but the other numbers are usually different.

edge

Each straight side of a polygon is called an edge.

For example, the edges of this polygon are segments AB, BC, CD, DE, and EA.

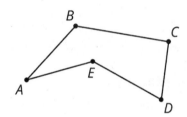

equivalent expressions

Equivalent expressions are always equal to each other. If the expressions have variables, they are equal whenever the same value is used for the variable in each expression.

For example, $3x + 4x$ is equivalent to $5x + 2x$. No matter what value we use for x, these expressions are always equal. When x is 3, both expressions equal 21. When x is 10, both expressions equal 70.

equivalent ratios

Two ratios are equivalent if you can multiply each of the numbers in the first ratio by the same factor to get the numbers in the second ratio. For example, $8 : 6$ is equivalent to $4 : 3$, because $8 \cdot \frac{1}{2} = 4$ and $6 \cdot \frac{1}{2} = 3$.

iM KH

A recipe for lemonade says to use 8 cups of water and 6 lemons. If we use 4 cups of water and 3 lemons, it will make half as much lemonade. Both recipes taste the same, because and are equivalent ratios.

cups of water	number of lemons
8	6
4	3

exponent

In expressions like 5^3 and 8^2, the 3 and the 2 are called exponents. They tell you how many factors to multiply. For example, $5^3 = 5 \cdot 5 \cdot 5$, and $8^2 = 8 \cdot 8$.

face

Each flat side of a polyhedron is called a face. For example, a cube has 6 faces, and they are all squares.

frequency

The frequency of a data value is how many times it occurs in the data set.

For example, there were 20 dogs in a park. The table shows the frequency of each color.

color	frequency
white	4
brown	7
black	3
multi-color	6

greatest common factor

The greatest common factor of two numbers is the largest number that divides evenly into both numbers. Sometimes we call this the GCF. For example, 15 is the greatest common factor of 45 and 60.

- The factors of 45 are 1, 3, 5, 9, *15*, and 45.

- The factors of 60 are 1, 2, 3, 4, 5, 6, 10, 12, *15*, 20, 30, and 60.

height (of a parallelogram or triangle)

The height is the shortest distance from the base of the shape to the opposite side (for a parallelogram) or opposite vertex (for a triangle).

We can show the height in more than one place, but it will always be perpendicular to the chosen base.

histogram

A histogram is a way to represent data on a number line. Data values are grouped by ranges. The height of the bar shows how many data values are in that group.

This histogram shows there were 10 people who earned 2 or 3 tickets. We can't tell how many of them earned 2 tickets or how many earned 3. Each bar includes the left-end value but not the right-end value. (There were 5 people who earned 0 or 1 tickets and 13 people who earned 6 or 7 tickets.)

iV KH

independent variable

The independent variable is used to calculate the value of another variable.

For example, a boat travels at a constant speed of 25 miles per hour. The equation $d = 25t$ describes the relationship between the boat's distance and time. The independent variable is time, because t is multiplied by 25 to get d.

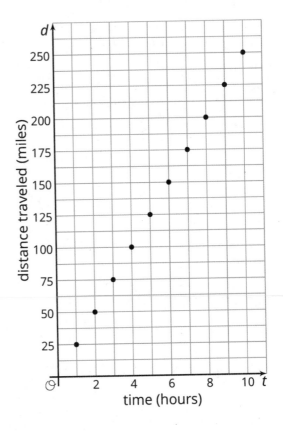

interquartile range (IQR)

The interquartile range is one way to measure how spread out a data set is. We sometimes call this the IQR. To find the interquartile range we subtract the first quartile from the third quartile.

For example, the IQR of this data set is 20 because $50 - 30 = 20$.

22	29	30	31	32	43	44	45	50	50	59
		Q1			Q2			Q3		

least common multiple

The least common multiple of two numbers is the smallest product you can get by multiplying each of the two numbers by some whole number. Sometimes we call this the LCM. For example, 30 is the least common multiple of 6 and 10.

- The multiples of 6 are 6, 12, 18, 24, *30*, 36, 42, 48, 54, 60 . . .

- The multiples of 10 are 10, 20, *30*, 40, 50, 60, 70, 80 . . .

long division

Long division is a way to show the steps for dividing numbers in decimal form. It finds the quotient one digit at a time, from left to right.

For example, here is the long division for $57 \div 4$.

$$
\begin{array}{r}
14.25 \\
4\overline{)57.00} \\
-4 \\
\hline
17 \\
-16 \\
\hline
10 \\
-8 \\
\hline
20 \\
-20 \\
\hline
0
\end{array}
$$

mean

The mean is one way to measure the center of a data set. We can think of it as a balance point. For example, for the data set 7, 9, 12, 13, 14, the mean is 11.

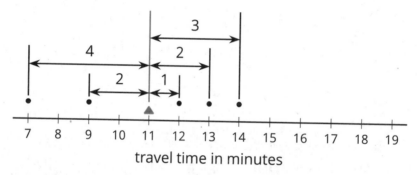

travel time in minutes

To find the mean, add up all the numbers in the data set. Then, divide by how many numbers there are. $7 + 9 + 12 + 13 + 14 = 55$ and $55 \div 5 = 11$.

mean absolute deviation (MAD)

The mean absolute deviation is one way to measure how spread out a data set is. Sometimes we call this the MAD. For example, for the data set 7, 9, 12, 13, 14, the MAD is 2.4. This tells us that these travel times are typically 2.4 minutes away from the mean, which is 11.

travel time in minutes

iM KH

To find the MAD, add up the distance between each data point and the mean. Then, divide by how many numbers there are.

$4 + 2 + 1 + 2 + 3 = 12$ and $12 \div 5 = 2.4$

measure of center
A measure of center is a value that seems typical for a data distribution.

Mean and median are both measures of center.

median
The median is one way to measure the center of a data set. It is the middle number when the data set is listed in order.

For the data set 7, 9, 12, 13, 14, the median is 12.

For the data set 3, 5, 6, 8, 11, 12, there are two numbers in the middle. The median is the average of these two numbers. $6 + 8 = 14$ and $14 \div 2 = 7$.

meters per second
Meters per second is a unit for measuring speed. It tells how many meters an object goes in one second.

For example, a person walking 3 meters per second is going faster than another person walking 2 meters per second.

negative number
A negative number is a number that is less than zero. On a horizontal number line, negative numbers are usually shown to the left of 0.

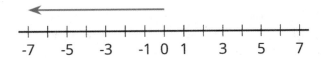

net
A net is a two-dimensional figure that can be folded to make a polyhedron.

Here is a net for a cube.

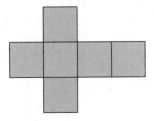

numerical data

A set of numerical data has values that are numbers.

For example, Han lists the ages of people in his family: 7, 10, 12, 36, 40, 67.

opposite

Two numbers are opposites if they are the same distance from 0 and on different sides of the number line.

For example, 4 is the opposite of -4, and -4 is the opposite of 4. They are both the same distance from 0. One is negative, and the other is positive.

opposite vertex

For each side of a triangle, there is one vertex that is not on that side. This is the opposite vertex.

For example, point A is the opposite vertex to side BC.

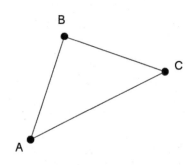

pace

Pace is one way to describe how fast something is moving. Pace tells how much time it takes the object to travel a certain distance.

For example, Diego walks at a pace of 10 minutes per mile. Elena walks at a pace of 11 minutes per mile. Elena walks slower than Diego, because it takes her more time to travel the same distance.

parallelogram

A parallelogram is a type of quadrilateral that has two pairs of parallel sides.

Here are two examples of parallelograms.

per

The word *per* means "for each." For example, if the price is $5 per ticket, that means you will pay $5 *for each* ticket. Buying 4 tickets would cost $20, because $4 \cdot 5 = 20$.

percent

The word *percent* means "for each 100." The symbol for percent is %.

For example, a quarter is worth 25 cents, and a dollar is worth 100 cents. We can say that a quarter is worth 25% of a dollar.

percentage

A percentage is a rate per 100.

For example, a fish tank can hold 36 liters. Right now there is 27 liters of water in the tank. The percentage of the tank that is full is 75%.

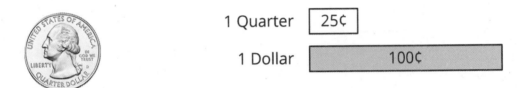

polygon

A polygon is a closed, two-dimensional shape with straight sides that do not cross each other.

Figure $ABCDE$ is an example of a polygon.

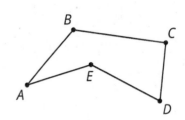

polyhedron

A polyhedron is a closed, three-dimensional shape with flat sides. When we have more than one polyhedron, we call them polyhedra.

Here are some drawings of polyhedra.

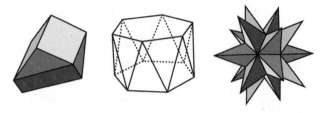

positive number

A positive number is a number that is greater than zero. On a horizontal number line, positive numbers are usually shown to the right of 0.

prism

A prism is a type of polyhedron that has two bases that are identical copies of each other. The bases are connected by rectangles or parallelograms.

Here are some drawings of prisms.

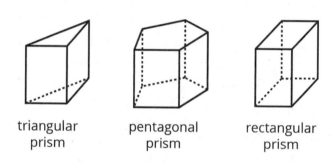

triangular
prism

pentagonal
prism

rectangular
prism

pyramid

A pyramid is a type of polyhedron that has one base. All the other faces are triangles, and they all meet at a single vertex.

iM KH

Here are some drawings of pyramids.

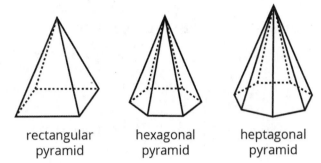

rectangular pyramid   hexagonal pyramid   heptagonal pyramid

quadrant

The coordinate plane is divided into 4 regions called quadrants. The quadrants are numbered using Roman numerals, starting in the top right corner.

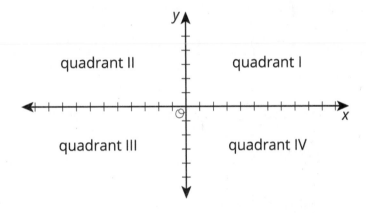

quadrilateral

A quadrilateral is a type of polygon that has 4 sides. A rectangle is an example of a quadrilateral. A pentagon is not a quadrilateral, because it has 5 sides.

quartile

Quartiles are the numbers that divide a data set into four sections that each have the same number of values.

For example, in this data set the first quartile is 30. The second quartile is the same thing as the median, which is 43. The third quartile is 50.

22	29	30	31	32	43	44	45	50	50	59
		Q1			Q2			Q3		

range

The range is the distance between the smallest and largest values in a data set. For example, for the data set 3, 5, 6, 8, 11, 12, the range is 9, because $12 - 3 = 9$.

ratio

A ratio is an association between two or more quantities.

For example, the ratio 3 : 2 could describe a recipe that uses 3 cups of flour for every 2 eggs, or a boat that moves 3 meters every 2 seconds. One way to represent the ratio 3 : 2 is with a diagram that has 3 blue squares for every 2 green squares.

rational number

A rational number is a fraction or the opposite of a fraction.

For example, 8 and -8 are rational numbers because they can be written as $\frac{8}{1}$ and $-\frac{8}{1}$.

Also, 0.75 and -0.75 are rational numbers because they can be written as $\frac{75}{100}$ and $-\frac{75}{100}$.

reciprocal

Dividing 1 by a number gives the reciprocal of that number. For example, the reciprocal of 12 is $\frac{1}{12}$, and the reciprocal of $\frac{2}{5}$ is $\frac{5}{2}$.

region

A region is the space inside of a shape. Some examples of two-dimensional regions are inside a circle or inside a polygon. Some examples of three-dimensional regions are the inside of a cube or the inside of a sphere.

same rate

We use the words *same rate* to describe two situations that have equivalent ratios.

For example, a sink is filling with water at a rate of 2 gallons per minute. If a tub is also filling with water at a rate of 2 gallons per minute, then the sink and the tub are filling at the same rate.

sign

The sign of any number other than 0 is either positive or negative.

For example, the sign of 6 is positive. The sign of -6 is negative. Zero does not have a sign, because it is not positive or negative.

solution to an equation

A solution to an equation is a number that can be used in place of the variable to make the equation true.

For example, 7 is the solution to the equation $m + 1 = 8$, because it is true that $7 + 1 = 8$. The solution to $m + 1 = 8$ is not 9, because $9 + 1 \neq 8$.

solution to an inequality
A solution to an inequality is a number that can be used in place of the variable to make the inequality true.

For example, 5 is a solution to the inequality $c < 10$, because it is true that $5 < 10$. Some other solutions to this inequality are 9.9, 0, and -4.

speed
Speed is one way to describe how fast something is moving. Speed tells how much distance the object travels in a certain amount of time.

For example, Tyler walks at a speed of 4 miles per hour. Priya walks at a speed of 5 miles per hour. Priya walks faster than Tyler, because she travels more distance in the same amount of time.

spread
The spread of a set of numerical data tells how far apart the values are.

For example, the dot plots show that the travel times for students in South Africa are more spread out than for New Zealand.

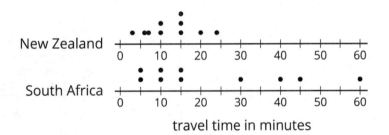

squared
We use the word *squared* to mean "to the second power." This is because a square with side length s has an area of $s \cdot s$, or s^2.

statistical question
A statistical question can be answered by collecting data that has variability. Here are some examples of statistical questions:

- Who is the most popular musical artist at your school?

- When do students in your class typically eat dinner?

- Which classroom in your school has the most books?

surface area

The surface area of a polyhedron is the number of square units that covers all the faces of the polyhedron, without any gaps or overlaps.

For example, if the faces of a cube each have an area of 9 cm^2, then the surface area of the cube is $6 \cdot 9$, or 54 cm^2.

table

A table organizes information into horizontal *rows* and vertical *columns*. The first row or column usually tells what the numbers represent.

For example, here is a table showing the tail lengths of three different pets. This table has four rows and two columns.

pet	tail length (inches)
dog	22
cat	12
mouse	2

tape diagram

A tape diagram is a group of rectangles put together to represent a relationship between quantities.

For example, this tape diagram shows a ratio of 30 gallons of yellow paint to 50 gallons of blue paint.

10	10	10

10	10	10	10	10

If each rectangle were labeled 5, instead of 10, then the same picture could represent the equivalent ratio of 15 gallons of yellow paint to 25 gallons of blue paint.

term

A term is a part of an expression. It can be a single number, a variable, or a number and a variable that are multiplied together. For example, the expression $5x + 18$ has two terms. The first term is $5x$ and the second term is 18.

unit price

The unit price is the cost for one item or for one unit of measure. For example, if 10 feet of chain link fencing cost \$150, then the unit price is $150 \div 10$, or \$15 per foot.

unit rate

A unit rate is a rate per 1.

iM KH

For example, 12 people share 2 pies equally. One unit rate is 6 people per pie, because $12 \div 2 = 6$. The other unit rate is $\frac{1}{6}$ of a pie per person, because $2 \div 12 = \frac{1}{6}$.

variability

Variability means having different values.

For example, data set B has more variability than data set A. Data set B has many different values, while data set A has more of the same values.

A

B

variable

A variable is a letter that represents a number. You can choose different numbers for the value of the variable.

For example, in the expression $10 - x$, the variable is x. If the value of x is 3, then $10 - x = 7$, because $10 - 3 = 7$. If the value of x is 6, then $10 - x = 4$, because $10 - 6 = 4$.

vertex

A vertex is a point where two or more edges meet. When we have more than one vertex, we call them vertices.

The vertices in this polygon are labeled A, B, C, D, and E.

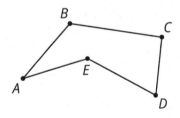

volume

Volume is the number of cubic units that fill a three-dimensional region, without any gaps or overlaps.

For example, the volume of this rectangular prism is 60 units^3, because it is composed of 3 layers that are each 20 units^3.

Attributions

"Notice and Wonder" and "I Notice/I Wonder" are trademarks of the National Council of Teachers of Mathematics, reflecting approaches developed by the Math Forum (http://www.nctm.org/mathforum/), and used here with permission.

Images that are not the original work of Illustrative Mathematics are in the public domain or released under a Creative Commons Attribution (CC-BY) license, and include an appropriate citation. Images that are the original work of Illustrative Mathematics do not include such a citation.

Image Attributions

studying, by English106. CC BY 2.0. Flickr. https://www.flickr.com/photos/english106/4357228667.

By JKpics. Public Domain. Pixabay. https://pixabay.com/en/worm-earthworm-pink-long-thin-1112176/.

By Clker-Free-Vector-Images. Public Domain. Pixabay. https://pixabay.com/en/cat-cartoon-art-pet-cute-animal-304204/.

Hawksbill Sea Turtle Carey de Concha (5840602412), by U.S. Fish and Wildlife Service Southeast Region. Public Domain. Wikimedia Commons. https://commons.wikimedia.org/wiki/File:Hawksbill_Sea_Turtle_Carey_de_Concha_(5840602412).jpg.

Pawsox Mascot, by Paul Keleher. CC BY 2.0. Wikimedia Commons. https://commons.wikimedia.org/wiki/File:Pawsox_mascot.jpg.

Notes

Notes